Focus in Grade 7
Teaching with Curriculum Focal Points

The Teaching with Curriculum Focal Points series consists of grade-level publications designed to support teachers, supervisors, and coordinators as they begin the discussion of a more focused curriculum across and within prekindergarten through grade 8, as presented in *Curriculum Focal Points for Prekindergarten through Grade 8 Mathematics*.

	ISBN #	NCTM stock #
Focus in Prekindergarten	978-0-87353-644-8	13626
Focus in Kindergarten	978-0-87353-645-5	13627
Focus in Grade 1	978-0-87353-646-2	13628
Focus in Grade 2	Coming Fall 2010	
Focus in Pre-K–2	978-0-87353-624-0	13486
Focus in Grade 3	978-0-87353-625-7	13487
Focus in Grade 4	978-0-87353-627-1	13490
Focus in Grade 5	978-0-87353-614-1	13437
Focus in Grades 3–5	978-0-87353-609-7	13395
Focus in Grade 6	978-0-87353-648-6	13630
Focus in Grade 8	978-0-87353-650-9	13632
Focus in Grades 6–8	978-0-87353-618-9	13465

Please visit www.nctm.org/catalog for details and ordering information.

Focus in Grade 7

Teaching with Curriculum Focal Points

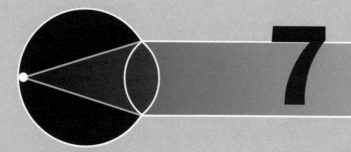

Jane F. Schielack, *Series Advisor*
Texas A&M University

NATIONAL COUNCIL OF
TEACHERS OF MATHEMATICS

Copyright © 2010 by
THE NATIONAL COUNCIL OF TEACHERS OF MATHEMATICS, INC.
1906 Association Drive, Reston, VA 20191-1502
(703) 620-9840; (800) 235-7566; www.nctm.org
All rights reserved

Library of Congress Cataloging-in-Publication Data

Focus in grade 7 : teaching with curriculum focal points / Jane F. Schielack, series advisor.
    p. cm.
 Includes bibliographical references.
 ISBN 978-0-87353-649-3 (alk. paper)
 1. Mathematics—Study and teaching (Elementary) —United States—Standards. 2. Seventh grade
(Education)—Curricula—United States—Standards. 3. Curriculum planning—United States. I.
Schielack, Jane F. II. National Council of Teachers of Mathematics. III. Title: Focus in grade seven.
 QA135.6.F6295 2010
 510.71'2—dc22
                                    2009045940

The National Council of Teachers of Mathematics is a public voice of mathematics education, supporting teachers to ensure equitable mathematics learning of the highest quality for all students through vision, leadership, professional development, and research.

Printed in the United States of America

Contents

Contents — Continued

On September 12, 2006, the National Council of Teachers of Mathematics released *Curriculum Focal Points for Prekindergarten through Grade 8 Mathematics: A Quest for Coherence* to encourage discussions at the national, state, and district levels on the importance of designing a coherent elementary mathematics curriculum focusing on the important mathematical ideas at each grade level. The natural question that followed the release of *Curriculum Focal Points* was "How do we translate this view of a focused curriculum into the classroom?"

Focus in Grade 7, one in a series of grade-level publications, is designed to support teachers, supervisors, and coordinators as they begin the discussion of a more focused curriculum across and within prekindergarten through grade 8, as presented in *Curriculum Focal Points. Focus in Grade 7*, in conjunction with the *Focus in Grade 6* and *Focus in Grade 8* books, will provide a strong foundation for mathematics in a focused curriculum across grades 6 through 8. Important mathematics to prepare students for grade 7 is addressed in the publications *Focus in Grade 3*, *Focus in Grade 4*, *Focus in Grade 5*, and *Focus in Grade 6*. Additionally, teacher educators should find *Focus in Grade 7* useful as a vehicle for exploring with their preservice teachers the mathematical ideas and curriculum issues related to the suggested grade 7 Curriculum Focal Points.

The contributors to, and reviewers of, these publications, all active leaders in mathematics education and professional development, guided the creation of this grade-level book as a framework for lesson-study experiences in which teachers deepen their understanding of the mathematical ideas they will be teaching. This book describes and illustrates instructional progressions for the mathematical concepts and skills of each grade 7 Curriculum Focal Point, including powerful representational supports for teaching and learning that can facilitate understanding, stimulate productive discussions about mathematical thinking, and provide a foundation for fluency with the core ideas. Because these instructional progressions cut across grades, you will see the progressions in each grade accompanied by summaries of progressions before and after that grade that connect to Focal Points and Connections in previous and following grades.

Whether you are working with your colleagues or individually, we hope that you will find the discussions of the instructional progressions, representations, problems, and lines of reasoning valuable as you plan activities and discussions for your students and as you strive to help your students achieve the depth of understanding of important mathematical concepts necessary for their future success.

—*Jane F. Schielack*
Series Advisor

To address the need for a prototypical, coherent, grade-level-specific mathematics curriculum linked to *Principles and Standards for School Mathematics* (NCTM 2000), the National Council of Teachers of Mathematics asked a team of mathematicians, mathematics educators, and school-based educators to identify three or four focal points in mathematics for each grade level, prekindergarten through grade 8. The writing team—consisting of at least one university-level mathematics educator or mathematician and one pre-K–8 classroom practitioner from each of the three grade bands (pre-K–grade 2, grades 3–5, and grades 6–8)—worked together to create a set of focal points that could serve as areas of emphasis for each grade level and be used as an outline for an articulated pre-K–8 mathematics curriculum. The members of the writing team based their decisions on recommendations from *Principles and Standards*, examinations of multiple curricula from several states and countries, and reviews of a wide array of researchers' and experts' writings on the subject.

We appreciate the contributions of all who have made this document possible.

On behalf of the Board of Directors,

Cathy Seeley
President (2004–2006)
National Council of Teachers of Mathematics

Francis (Skip) Fennell
President, 2006–2008
National Council of Teachers of Mathematics

Members of the Curriculum Focal Points for Grades PK–8 Writing Team

Jane F. Schielack, *Chair*, Texas A&M University, College Station, Texas
Sybilla Beckmann, University of Georgia, Athens, Georgia
Randall I. Charles, San José State University (emeritus), San José, California
Douglas H. Clements, University at Buffalo, State University of New York, Buffalo, New York
Paula B. Duckett, District of Columbia Public Schools (retired), Washington, D.C.
Francis (Skip) Fennell, McDaniel College, Westminster, Maryland
Sharon L. Lewandowski, Bryant Woods Elementary School, Columbia, Maryland
Cathy Seeley, Charles A. Dana Center, University of Texas at Austin, Austin, Texas
Emma Treviño, Charles A. Dana Center, University of Texas at Austin, Austin, Texas
Rose Mary Zbiek, The Pennsylvania State University, University Park, Pennsylvania

Staff Liaison
Melanie S. Ott, National Council of Teachers of Mathematics, Reston, Virginia

ACKNOWLEDGMENTS

The National Council of Teachers of Mathematics would like to thank the following individuals for developing a detailed outline of the content of this publication and for their reviews of, and feedback on, drafts of the manuscript. Special thanks go to Janie Schielack for all her time and support, her invaluable guidance and advice, and her continuing commitment to the Curriculum Focal Points project.

Series Advisor
Jane F. Schielack

Content Development
Words & Numbers
Baltimore, Maryland

Developers
Gladis Kersaint
University of South Florida

Connie Laughlin
Milwaukee, Wisconsin

Jim Lewis
University of Nebraska—Lincoln

Reviewers
Rose Mary Zbiek
Pennsylvania State University

Marshalyn Baker
Messalonskee Middle School
Oakland, Maine

1 Introduction

Purpose of This Guide

Your first question when looking at NCTM's Curriculum Focal Points might be "How can I use NCTM's Focal Points with the local and state curriculum I am expected to teach?" NCTM's Curriculum Focal Points are not intended to be a national curriculum but have been developed to help bring more consistency to mathematics curricula across the country. Collectively, they constitute a framework of how curricula might be organized at each grade level, prekindergarten through grade 8. They are also intended to help bring about discussion within and across states and school districts about the important mathematical ideas to be taught at each grade level. Because of the current variation among states' curricula, the Curriculum Focal Points are not likely to match up perfectly with any one state's curriculum. This volume explores the mathematics emphasized at grade 7 in the focused curriculum suggested by the NCTM Curriculum Focal Points framework. Additional grade-level and grade-band books are available from NCTM to help teachers translate the Curriculum Focal Points identified for their grade level into coherent and meaningful instruction. Taken together, this grade 7 guide, along with the grades 5, 6, and 8 guides and the grades 3–5 (Mirra 2008) and 6–8 (Mirra 2009) grade-band guides, can be used by groups of teachers in professional development experiences as well as by individual classroom teachers.

Purpose of Curriculum Focal Points

The mathematics curriculum in the United States has often been characterized as a "mile wide and an inch deep." Many topics are studied each year—often reviewing much that was covered in previous years—and little depth is added each time the topic is addressed. In addition, because education has always been locally controlled in the United States, learning expectations can significantly differ by state and local school systems. NCTM's *Curriculum Focal Points for Prekindergarten through Grade 8 Mathematics: A Quest for Coherence* (2006) is the next step in helping states and local districts refocus their curriculum. It provides an example of a focused and coherent curriculum in prekindergarten through grade 8 by identifying the most important mathematical topics, or "Focal Points," at each grade level. The Focal Points are not discrete topics to be taught and checked off, but rather a cluster of related knowledge, skills, and concepts. By organizing and prioritizing curriculum and instruction in prekindergarten–grade 8 around Focal Points at each grade level, teachers can foster more cumulative learning of mathematics by students, and students' work in the later grades will build on and deepen what they learned in the earlier grades. Organizing mathematics content in this

> *A curriculum is more than a collection of activities: It must be coherent, focused on important mathematics, and well articulated across the grades.*
>
> —The Curriculum Principle, *Principles and Standards for School Mathematics*

> It provides an example of a focused and coherent curriculum in prekindergarten through grade 8 by identifying the most important mathematical topics, or "Focal Points," at each grade level.

way will help ensure a solid mathematical foundation for high school mathematics and beyond.

Prior to the Curriculum Focal Points, the National Council of Teachers of Mathematics began the process of bringing about change to school mathematics programs in the 1980s, particularly with the first publication to outline standards in mathematics, titled *Curriculum and Evaluation Standards for School Mathematics* (NCTM 1989). That publication provided major direction to states and school districts in developing their curricula. NCTM's *Principles and Standards for School Mathematics* (2000) further elaborated the ideas of the 1989 Standards, outlining learning expectations in the grade bands of prekindergarten–2, 3–5, 6–8, and 9–12. *Principles and Standards* also highlighted six principles, which included the Curriculum Principle, to offer guidance for developing mathematics programs. The Curriculum Principle emphasized the need to link with, and build on, mathematical ideas as students progress through the grades, deepening their mathematical knowledge over time.

Impact of Focal Points on Curriculum, Instruction, and Assessment

Significant improvement can be made in the areas of curriculum, instruction, and assessment by identifying Focal Points at each grade level. At the curriculum level, Focal Points will allow for more rigorous and in-depth study of important mathematics at each grade level. This rigor will translate to a more meaningful curriculum that students can understand and apply. At the instructional level, Focal Points will allow teachers to more fully know the core topics they are responsible for teaching. Teachers will not be necessarily teaching *less* or *more* but will be able to teach *better*. Professional development can also be tailored to deepen teachers' knowledge of these Focal Points and connect these ideas in meaningful ways. Assessments can be designed that truly measure students' mastery of core topics rather than survey a broad range of disparate topics, thus allowing for closer monitoring of students' development. At the level of classroom assessment, having a smaller number of essential topics will help teachers have time to better determine what their students have learned and whether they have learned the material deeply enough to use and build on it in subsequent years. If state assessments are more focused as well, more detailed information can be gathered for districts and schools on areas for improvement.

Using This *Focus in Grade 7* Book

Many teachers tell us that they did not have an opportunity in their teacher preparation programs to build sufficient understanding of some of the mathematics topics that they now teach. The discussion of the mathematical ideas presented here is detailed enough for teachers to begin building understanding of the mathematics contained in each grade 7 Focal Point. To further understand what mathematics students are expected to learn before grade 7 and in later grades, teachers would benefit from examining the publications *Focus in Grade 6*, *Focus in Grade 8*, and *Focus in High School Mathematics: Reasoning and Sense Making* (NCTM 2009). We suggest that teachers form study groups (such as those in lesson study, mathematics circles, or other learning communities) to read and discuss parts of this publication, to work together to build a deeper understanding of the mathematics topics in each Focal Point, and to plan how to help their students develop such understanding by adapting as needed their present grade 7 teaching and learning strategies and materials. A helpful approach for other teacher working groups has been to share students' insights and questions and to look at students' work to understand different ways that students are solving problems, to address errors and misconceptions, and to help students move forward in a progression that fosters both understanding and fluency. Because teachers' lives are busy and demanding, the reader is better served by concentrating on small portions of this publication at a time and working through them deeply instead of trying to do too much at once and getting discouraged. Teachers' learning, like students' learning, is a continual process that can be very rewarding.

Bringing Focus into the Classroom: Instruction That Builds Understanding and Fluency

Although the main goal of this publication is to present in more detail the mathematical content in each of the Focal Points, some important pedagogical issues also need to be taken into account when creating an environment that supports focused instruction. Pedagogical principles for classrooms that do help students build understanding are outlined in *Principles and Standards for School Mathematics* (NCTM 2000) and in the National Research Council reports *Adding It Up* (Kilpatrick, Swafford, and Findell 2001) and *How Students Learn: Mathematics in the Classroom* (Donovan and Bransford 2005). An instructional environment that supports the development of understanding and fluency should be based on a logical progression of content that is connected across grades as well as within grades, should provide opportunities for students and teachers to engage in mathematically substantive discussions, and should involve teachers and students in interpreting and creating mathematical representations to enhance their understanding.

An instructional-progression approach

An instructional progression of concepts and skills supports coherence across and within grades. The table at the beginning of each Focal Point outlines the instructional progression and presents the mathematics suggested for grade 7 within the context of the related mathematics suggested for the grades before and after. Teacher study groups can work to identify gaps in the knowledge of their students that might be causing them difficulties with the mathematics in grade 7. In addition, the instructional progression offers a view of the future mathematics in which students will be applying the knowledge and skills learned in grade 7.

In-depth instructional conversations

Students have little opportunity to build understanding in a classroom in which the teacher does all the talking and explaining. A valuable instructional approach is one in which teachers create a nurturing, meaning-making community as students use "math talk" to discuss their mathematical thinking and help one another clarify their own mathematical thinking, understand and overcome errors, and describe the methods they use to solve problems (Fuson and Murata 2007). Such discussions identify commonalities and differences as well as advantages and disadvantages across methods. By having students talk about their own strategies, teachers can help them become aware of, and build on, their implicit informal knowledge (Lampert 1989; Mack 1990). As the teacher and students learn to listen respectfully to the math talk of others, they model, structure and clarify, instruct or explain, question, and give feedback to enhance one another's learning. As students' understanding and fluency in various topics increase, the amount and type of class discussion related to each topic will change. In-depth discussion of new topics should begin as more sophisticated, mature discussion of previously encountered topics continues.

Using mathematical representations

The use of mathematical representations, in particular mathematical drawings, during problem-solving discussions and explanations of mathematical thinking helps listeners better understand the speaker. The use of mathematical drawings as a component of homework and classwork by both students and the teacher helps them better understand each other's thinking and thus provides continual assessment to guide instruction as the teacher addresses issues that arise in such drawings and accompanying talk (e.g., errors or interesting mathematical thinking). Middle school teachers can use students' prior knowledge as a basis for building new understandings (Webb, Boswinkel, and Dekker 2008). Students can deepen their mathematical understandings by being led to make connections between their own representations that are "often grounded in ... experiences with real or imagined contexts" (p. 112) and new, less contextually bound representations purposefully introduced by the teacher. Examples are included throughout this publication as to how grade 7 teachers can help their students make the transition from concrete and numerical representations to algebraic reasoning, generalization, and abstract representations.

An Important Grade 7 Issue: Proportionality

The grade 7 Focal Point on proportionality is a crucial one. Proportionality is a concept that underlies many of the mathematics topics studied in grade 7. Students encounter proportionality in the use of scale factors to shrink and enlarge images, in the definition of similarity, in the justification of the existence of π, and in the applications of percent. The related section of this publication presents strategies that have students apply the concepts of ratio and proportionality in meaningful contexts. Students should be encouraged to connect their understandings of equivalent fractions and fraction representations of ratios to representations of situations involving proportions. Students should then be given many opportunities to use the representations to build meaning for generalizable procedures for finding equivalent ratios to solve a problem involving a proportional relationship, such as "How much will 5.5 pounds of gravel cost if 3 pounds cost $25?

Proportionality permeates the mathematics that students learn in grade 7 and in later grades. For example, students encounter proportionality in situations involving similar figures, constant rate of change, and slope in the graph of a linear function. Therefore, much attention should be dedicated to building meaning for the concept of proportionality and for the procedures used to solve for missing values in a proportion, with the goal being the ability to apply those concepts and procedures effectively in problem-solving situations.

The three grade 7 Focal Points and their Connections are reproduced on the following page.

Grade 7 Curriculum Focal Points

Number and Operations and Algebra and Geometry: **Developing an understanding of and applying proportionality, including similarity**

Students extend their work with ratios to develop an understanding of proportionality that they apply to solve single and multistep problems in numerous contexts. They use ratio and proportionality to solve a wide variety of percent problems, including problems involving discounts, interest, taxes, tips, and percent increase or decrease. They also solve problems about similar objects (including figures) by using scale factors that relate corresponding lengths of the objects or by using the fact that relationships of lengths within an object are preserved in similar objects. Students graph proportional relationships and identify the unit rate as the slope of the related line. They distinguish proportional relationships ($y/x = k$, or $y = kx$) from other relationships, including inverse proportionality ($xy = k$, or $y = k/x$).

Measurement and Geometry and Algebra: **Developing an understanding of and using formulas to determine surface areas and volumes of three-dimensional shapes**

By decomposing two- and three-dimensional shapes into smaller, component shapes, students find surface areas and develop and justify formulas for the surface areas and volumes of prisms and cylinders. As students decompose prisms and cylinders by slicing them, they develop and understand formulas for their volumes (*Volume = Area of base × Height*). They apply these formulas in problem solving to determine volumes of prisms and cylinders. Students see that the formula for the area of a circle is plausible by decomposing a circle into a number of wedges and rearranging them into a shape that approximates a parallelogram. They select appropriate two- and three-dimensional shapes to model real-world situations and solve a variety of problems (including multistep problems) involving surface areas, areas and circumferences of circles, and volumes of prisms and cylinders.

Number and Operations and Algebra: **Developing an understanding of operations on all rational numbers and solving linear equations**

Students extend understandings of addition, subtraction, multiplication, and division, together with their properties, to all rational numbers, including negative integers. By applying properties of arithmetic and considering negative numbers in everyday contexts (e.g., situations of owing money or measuring elevations above and below sea level), students explain why the rules for adding, subtracting, multiplying, and dividing with negative numbers make sense. They use the arithmetic of rational numbers as they formulate and solve linear equations in one variable and use these equations to solve problems. Students make strategic choices of procedures to solve linear equations in one variable and implement them efficiently, understanding that when they use the properties of equality to express an equation in a new way, solutions that they obtain for the new equation also solve the original equation.

Connections to the Focal Points

Measurement and Geometry: Students connect their work on proportionality with their work on area and volume by investigating similar objects. They understand that if a scale factor describes how corresponding lengths in two similar objects are related, then the square of the scale factor describes how corresponding areas are related, and the cube of the scale factor describes how corresponding volumes are related. Students apply their work on proportionality to measurement in different contexts, including converting among different units of measurement to solve problems involving rates such as motion at a constant speed. They also apply proportionality when they work with the circumference, radius, and diameter of a circle; when they find the area of a sector of a circle; and when they make scale drawings.

Number and Operations: In grade 4, students used equivalent fractions to determine the decimal representations of fractions that they could represent with terminating decimals. Students now use division to express any fraction as a decimal, including fractions that they must represent with infinite decimals. They find this method useful when working with proportions, especially those involving percents. Students connect their work with dividing fractions to solving equations of the form $ax = b$, where a and b are fractions. Students continue to develop their understanding of multiplication and division and the structure of numbers by determining if a counting number greater than 1 is a prime, and if it is not, by factoring it into a product of primes.

Data Analysis: Students use proportions to make estimates relating to a population on the basis of a sample. They apply percentages to make and interpret histograms and circle graphs.

Probability: Students understand that when all outcomes of an experiment are equally likely, the theoretical probability of an event is the fraction of outcomes in which the event occurs. Students use theoretical probability and proportions to make approximate predictions.

Reprinted from *Curriculum Focal Points for Prekindergarten through Grade 8 Mathematics: A Quest for Coherence* (Reston, Va.: NCTM, 2006, p. 19).

In grade 7, students develop an understanding of proportionality and apply that understanding to solve problems involving proportional relationships, including similarity. The goal is for students to be able to write a proportion to represent a problem involving proportionality and use the properties of proportionality to solve the problem.

Instructional Progression for Proportionality

The focus on proportionality in grade 7 is supported by a progression of related mathematical ideas before and after grade 7, as shown in table 2.1. To give perspective to the grade 7 work, we first discuss some of the important ideas that students focused on before grade 7 that prepare them for learning about proportionality in grade 7. At the end of the detailed discussion of this grade 7 Focal Point, we present examples of how students will use their proportionality understandings and skills in later grades. For more detailed discussions of the "before" and "after" parts of the instructional progression, please see the appropriate grade-level books, for example, *Focus in Grade 3, Focus in Grade 4, Focus in Grade 5, Focus in Grade 6*, and *Focus in Grade 8*.

Table 2.1 represents an instructional progression for the conceptual understanding of proportionality before grade 7, during grade 7, and after grade 7.

Early Foundations of Proportionality

Students develop skills and understandings prior to grade 7 that they can use as they work with the concepts of proportionality taught in grade 7. Students have previously applied multiplicative thinking, developed an understanding of ratios including equivalent ratios, and solved ratio and rate problems using a variety of strategies involving multiplication and division. All these skills work together to facilitate students' understanding of the concepts in this Focal Point.

In grade 6, students strengthen and apply their understanding of multiplicative reasoning. That is, they understand that *2 times* has a different meaning than *2 more than*, *3 times* has a different meaning than *3 more than*, and so on. As students analyze and compare the representations shown in tables and in graphs with the same scales, as shown in figure 2.1, they begin to see the differences between an additive relationship and a multiplicative relationship.

Table 2.1
Grade 7: Focusing on Proportionality—Instructional Progression for Proportionality

Before Grade 7	Grade 7	After Grade 7
Students develop multiplicative thinking. Students develop an understanding of equivalent ratios. Students solve rate and ratio problems using a variety of strategies involving multiplication and division.	Students develop an understanding of proportional relationships. Students graph proportional relationships and recognize the graph as a line through the origin with the constant of proportionality as the slope of the line. Students express proportional relationships as $y = kx$ and distinguish them from other relationships, such as $y = kx + b$, where $b \neq 0$. Students use understanding of percent as a ratio to solve a variety of problems including problems involving discounts, interest, taxes, tips, and percent of increase or decrease. Students develop an understanding of similarity as a geometric relationship involving proportionality in which scale factors can be used to solve problems, for example, finding lengths in similar figures, distances on maps, and so on. Students use proportionality to understand π and its use in determining the circumference and area of a circle.* Students use their knowledge of proportionality to solve a wide range of problems involving ratios and rates.	Students understand the relationships among the angle measures, side lengths, perimeters, areas, and volumes of similar objects and use these relationships to solve problems. Students understand the relationship of a line's slope to the similar triangles formed by using two points on the line as two vertices of a right triangle and the intersection of the "rise" and "run" segments related to those two points as the third vertex.**

*Appears in the Grade 7 Connections to the Focal Points (NCTM 2006).
**Appears in the Grade 8 Connections to the Focal Points (NCTM 2006).

In grade 6, students also explore multiplication as scaling. When a quantity is multiplied by a number greater than 1, it is scaled up. When a number is multiplied by a positive number less than 1, it is scaled down. When a number is multiplied by 1, the identity element for multiplication, the number remains the same. The number by which you multiply is called the *scaling factor* (or *scale factor*).

In grade 6, the focus on ratio and rate plays an important role in students' building the foundation necessary to understand proportionality. Students learn that a ratio is a multiplicative comparison of two numbers, and they build from what they know about fractions to understand ratios. For example, students use ratios to represent part-to-whole relationships, part-to-part relationships, and whole-to-part relationships, as is illustrated in figure 2.2.

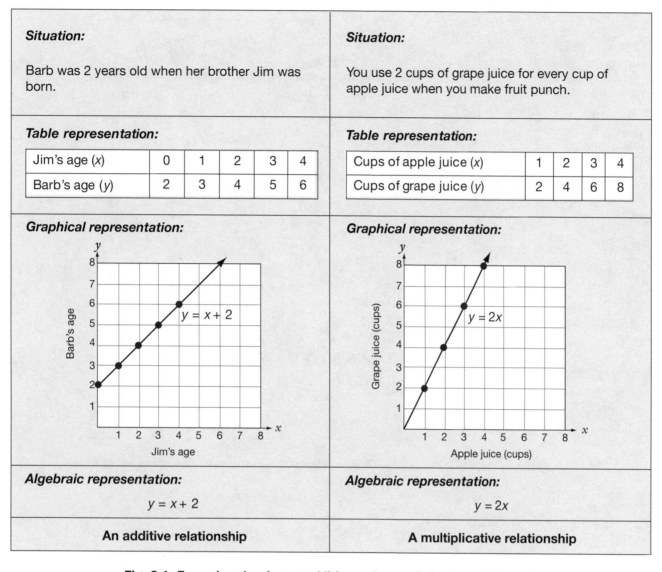

Fig. 2.1. Examples showing an additive and a multiplicative relationship

Students also use their understanding of equivalent fractions to determine whether two ratios are equivalent, that is, whether the resulting fractions are equal. They learn that equivalent ratios represent the same multiplicative comparison. They use various methods to model equivalent ratios, as shown in figure 2.3.

In grade 6, students use a type of ratio, called a *rate*, to describe a comparison of two measurements that often involve different units, as shown in figure 2.4.

Students also write a rate as a unit rate, that is, as an equivalent ratio with a denominator of 1 unit. Students learn that every rate situation can be written in two ways with two different unit rates. For example, in the situation in which you can buy 6 pounds of apples for $3, the relationship can be described as the rate

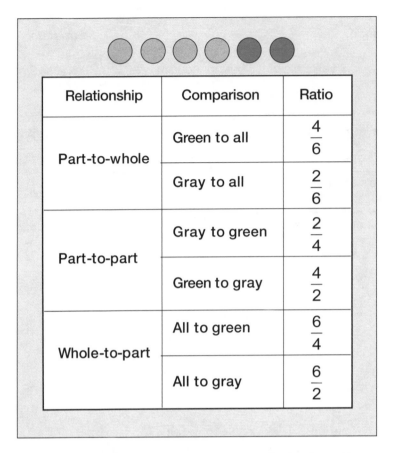

Relationship	Comparison	Ratio
Part-to-whole	Green to all	$\dfrac{4}{6}$
	Gray to all	$\dfrac{2}{6}$
Part-to-part	Gray to green	$\dfrac{2}{4}$
	Green to gray	$\dfrac{4}{2}$
Whole-to-part	All to green	$\dfrac{6}{4}$
	All to gray	$\dfrac{6}{2}$

Fig. 2.2. Relationships that can be described using ratios

$$\frac{6 \text{ pounds}}{3 \text{ dollars}}$$

and as the unit rate in terms of pounds per dollar: 2 pounds per dollar or

$$\frac{2 \text{ pounds}}{1 \text{ dollar}}.$$

The same situation can be described by the rate

$$\frac{3 \text{ dollars}}{6 \text{ pounds}}$$

and as the unit rate in terms of dollars per pound:

$$\frac{1}{2} \text{ dollar per pound or } \frac{\frac{1}{2} \text{ dollar}}{1 \text{ pound}}, \ \frac{0.50 \text{ dollar}}{1 \text{ pound}}, \text{ or } \frac{\$0.50}{1 \text{ pound}}.$$

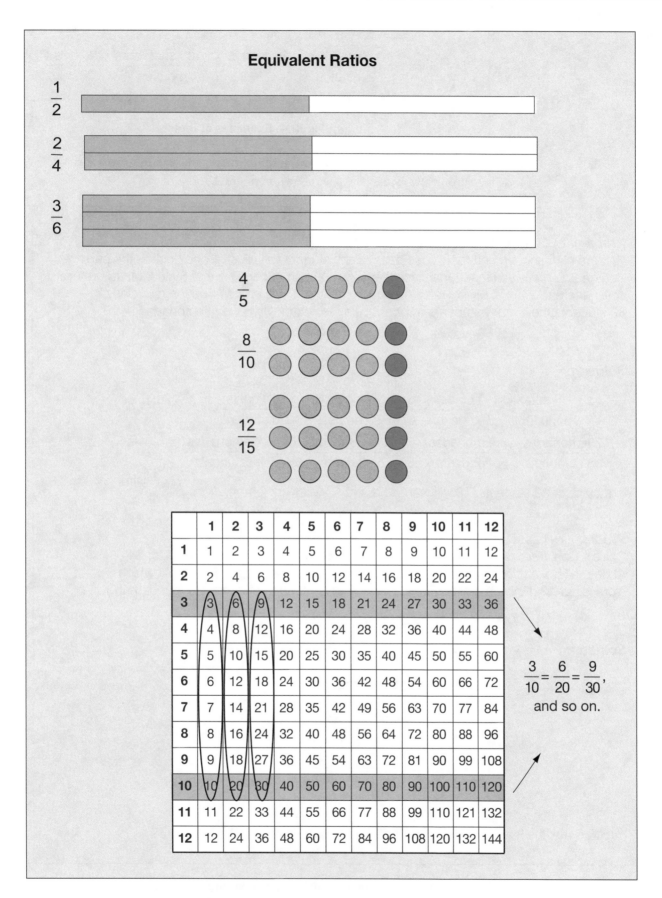

Fig. 2.3. Representations of equivalent ratios

$$\text{Rates:} \quad \frac{80 \text{ words}}{2 \text{ minutes}} \quad \frac{48 \text{ inches}}{4 \text{ feet}} \quad \frac{100 \text{ students}}{4 \text{ buses}} \quad \frac{20 \text{ miles}}{3 \text{ hours}}$$

Fig. 2.4. Examples of rates

Students then use their understanding of ratio and rate to solve a variety of problems, such as the ones shown in figure 2.5.

Problem 1: Class Party Problem

You are planning a menu for a class party. Each student will receive one drink at the party. Your teacher tells you that, for a class this size, you can expect 3 out of 5 students to prefer cola, whereas 2 out of 5 will prefer lemonade. If, in fact, this proves true for your class of 30 students, how many students will want cola? How many will want lemonade?

Solution:

$$\frac{3 \text{ colas}}{5 \text{ students}} = \frac{3 \text{ colas}}{5 \text{ students}} \times \frac{6}{6} = \frac{3 \text{ colas} \times 6}{5 \text{ students} \times 6} = \frac{18 \text{ colas}}{30 \text{ students}}$$

$$\frac{2 \text{ lemonades}}{5 \text{ students}} = \frac{2 \text{ lemonades}}{5 \text{ students}} \times \frac{6}{6} = \frac{2 \text{ lemonades} \times 6}{5 \text{ students} \times 6} = \frac{12 \text{ lemonades}}{30 \text{ students}}$$

In a class of 30 students, 18 will want cola and 12 will want lemonade.

Problem 2: Least Unit Price Problem

Callie's Cats sells cat food for $0.89 a can. Pet Mart sells 5 cans of cat food for $4.00. At Jay's Pets, cat food is 8 cans for $6.50. The cans are all the same size. At which store is cat food the least expensive? (Remember, fractions of cents are rounded up.)

Solution:

$$\text{Callie's Cats:} \quad \frac{\$0.89}{1 \text{ can}}$$

$$\text{Pet Mart:} \quad \frac{\$4.00}{5 \text{ cans}} = \frac{\$0.80}{1 \text{ can}}$$

$$\text{Jay's Pets:} \quad \frac{\$6.50}{8 \text{ cans}} = \frac{\$0.82}{1 \text{ can}}$$

Pet Mart has the least expensive cat food when compared by unit price.

Fig. 2.5. Sample problems involving ratio and rate

Focusing on Understanding and Applying Proportionality

As students begin their exploration of proportionality in grade 7, it is important that they understand the language associated with proportions and proportional reasoning. Students also need to be able to distinguish proportional relationships from relationships that are not proportional. The goal is for students to gain the ability to use proportions to solve problems. When proportionality becomes a focus in the curriculum in grade 7, students begin to see proportional relationships in problems that they previously solved.

> ## Reflect As You Read
>
> **Considering the importance of understanding ratios and rates as essential background knowledge, reflect on your school's curriculum and how much your students know about these topics prior to the grade 7 focus on proportionality.**

Using language to develop understanding of proportionality

As students begin to develop an understanding of proportionality, they need to understand and properly use related mathematical terms, such as *ratio*, *rate*, *proportion*, *proportionality*, *proportional relationship*, *unit rate*, *constant of proportionality*, and *scale factor*.

A *proportion* is an equation stating that two ratios are equivalent. For example,

$$\frac{3}{4} = \frac{6}{8}$$

can be interpreted as a proportion stating that the ratios 3/4 (3 to 4) and 6/8 (6 to 8) are equivalent. This proportion can be thought of as "3 is to 4 as 6 is to 8." Because a proportion is a statement that two ratios are equivalent, students can build on their understanding of ratios and equivalent ratios to develop an understanding of a proportion. The term *proportionality* refers to the property that one quantity is a constant times another. A *proportional relationship* exists when a relationship between two quantities can be described by a set of equivalent ratios. *Proportional reasoning* is used along with known quantities to find unknown quantities.

A teacher might introduce the characteristics of a proportional relationship to students using the following situation:

Suppose you walked 3 miles in 1 hour. Now suppose that you repeated this for a second hour and a third hour and a fourth hour.

The instructional goal is for students, after working with proportionality over time in various contexts, to be able to summarize, in their own words, the following ideas about the given proportional relationship:

- With the additional assumption that all the walking takes place at the same speed, the distance traveled is proportional to the time elapsed, and for elapsed time period "x", the distance traveled is "$3x$," so the proportional relationship can be represented with the equation $y = 3x$.

- Substituting the elapsed time values 1, 2, 3, and 4 into the equation for x gives the related distance-traveled values 3, 6, 9, and 12.

- A table that includes the ordered pairs (1, 3), (2, 6), (3, 9), (4, 12) is a partial representation of the proportional relationship.

- The points located by these ordered pairs lie on a line that goes through the origin that is described by the equation $y = 3x$.

- The ratios $y:x$ for every point on the line are equivalent.

To help students reach this learning goal, teachers can provide opportunities for students to engage in the following types of experiences and discussions.

In the given situation, the proportional relationship described is between distance traveled and time elapsed. Students should notice that one may choose any two distance-time pairs and use them to write a proportion. For example, students may choose 3 miles in 1 hour and 6 miles in 2 hours and can write the proportion

$$\frac{3 \text{ miles}}{1 \text{ hour}} = \frac{6 \text{ miles}}{2 \text{ hours}}.$$

Students also can write

$$\frac{3}{1} = \frac{6}{2}$$

if the measurement units of miles and hours are understood.

The ratios 3 miles/1 hour and 6 miles/2 hours are representations of a *rate;* each is a ratio of two quantities that, in this situation, are measured in different units. A *unit rate* is a rate in which the numerical part of the denominator is 1, so 3 miles/1 hour is a unit rate. The numerical part of the numerator of a unit rate can be called the *constant of proportionality* for that proportional relationship. In the proportional relationship represented by

$$\frac{3 \text{ miles}}{1 \text{ hour}} = \frac{6 \text{ miles}}{2 \text{ hours}},$$

the constant of proportionality is 3 when comparing distance traveled in miles to elapsed time in hours; that is, the distance traveled in miles is 3 times the number of hours of time elapsed. The constant of proportionality is also called the *scale factor.*

By observing the patterns in a set of equivalent ratios that describe a proportional relationship, students may conjecture that the relationship between the numerators (y) and denominators (x) of the equivalent ratios can be described by the equation

$$y = kx \text{ or } \frac{y}{x} = k,$$

(which are equivalent except when $x = 0$) where k represents the constant of proportionality (or scale factor) of the relationship. The proportional relationship that exists when $k = 1$ is represented by the equation $y = x$. In the distance-time relationship represented by the equivalent ratios

$$\frac{3 \text{ miles}}{1 \text{ hour}} = \frac{6 \text{ miles}}{2 \text{ hours}} = \frac{9 \text{ miles}}{3 \text{ hours}} = \frac{12 \text{ miles}}{4 \text{ hours}},$$

the proportional relationship can be represented by the equations

$$y = 3x$$

and

$$\frac{y}{x} = 3,$$

so the constant of proportionality, or scale factor, is 3.

For any ratio that describes a relationship, another ratio can be formed using the reciprocal to describe an equivalent relationship. For example, the relationship described by the proportion

$$\frac{3 \text{ miles}}{1 \text{ hour}} = \frac{6 \text{ miles}}{2 \text{ hours}}$$

can also be described by a proportion using the reciprocals of the ratios:

$$\frac{1 \text{ hour}}{3 \text{ miles}} = \frac{2 \text{ hours}}{6 \text{ miles}}.$$

The unit rate for this second proportion can be obtained by dividing the numerator and denominator by 3:

$$\frac{1 \text{ hour} \div 3}{3 \text{ miles} \div 3} = \frac{\frac{1}{3} \text{ hour}}{1 \text{ mile}},$$

or

$$\frac{1}{3} \text{ hour per mile.}$$

The constant of proportionality, k, is 1/3 when comparing hours of time elapsed to miles traveled; that is, the number of hours elapsed is 1/3 times the number of miles traveled. Figure 2.6 shows in table form and graphically the two representations of the proportional relationship in the given hiking situation. As students explore proportional relationships, they learn that the points in the graph of any given proportional relationship are collinear and lie on a line that passes through the origin.

Comparing proportional relationships with relationships that are not proportional

As students focus on proportionality, they begin to develop the ability to distinguish between relationships that are proportional and relationships that are not proportional. A proportional relationship is described by a constant of proportionality. Figure 2.7 shows two linear relationships; one is a proportional relationship and one is not a proportional relationship.

The equation $y = 2x$ that models the relationship in the left-hand column of figure 2.7 is in the form $y = kx$ and models a proportional relationship in which k, the constant of proportionality, is equal to 2. The equation $y = 2x + 2.50$ that models the relationship in the right-hand column of figure 2.7 is in the form $y = mx + b$. An equation in this form models a linear relationship but not a proportional relationship—unless $b = 0$. If $b = 0$, the equation $y = mx + b$ is equivalent to $y = mx$, which models a proportional relationship whose constant of proportionality is represented by m rather than k. A proportional relationship is a special case of a linear relationship. The graph of a linear relationship is a line; if that line is not vertical and passes through the origin, then the linear relationship is also a proportional relationship. Examples of other relationships that involve multiplication but are not proportional are shown in figure 2.8.

Students can distinguish proportional relationships from relationships that are not proportional by analyzing the graph of the relationship. The ratio of any x-value to its corresponding y-value should be equivalent to the ratio of any other x-value to its corresponding y-value. In a proportional relationship, every y-value is a product of the constant of proportionality, k, times the corresponding x-value. But in a relationship that is not proportional, no constant of proportionality is involved. Thus, we recognize that a relationship is not proportional when we learn that the ratio y/x can be different for different points (x, y), as illustrated in figure 2.9.

Reflect As You Read

How would your students think about this problem:

You buy 2 packages of trading cards for $6. How much would it cost to buy 10 packages?

What representations are they comfortable using? Can they reason through any procedures for solving this problem?

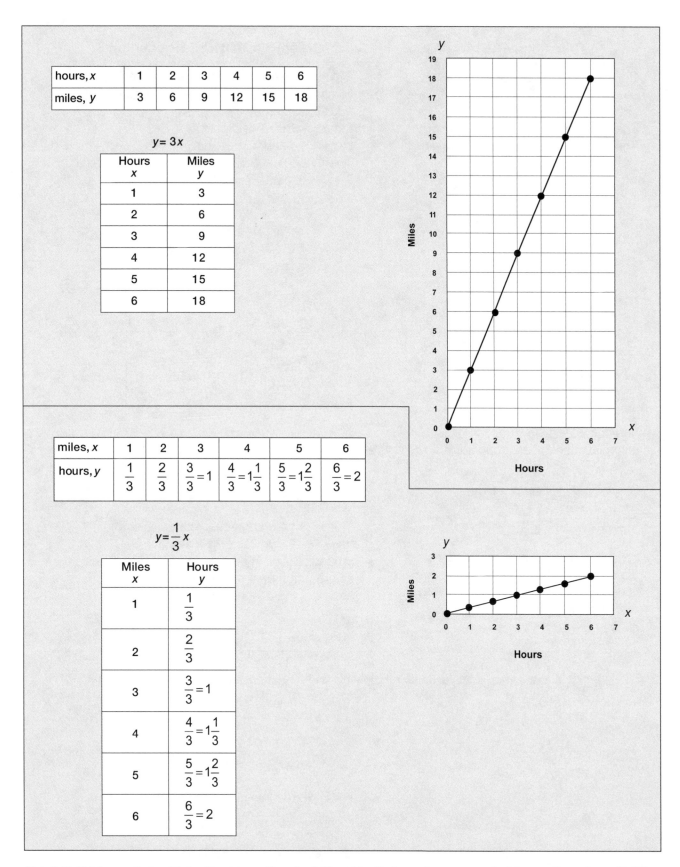

Fig. 2.6. Tables and graphs for the proportional relationship that can be represented by $y = 3x$ and $y = (1/3)x$, where the constants of proportionality are $k = 3$ and $k = 1/3$

17

Proportional Relationship	Relationship That Is Not Proportional
Chicken costs $2 per pound. Let y = number of dollars. Let x = number of pounds. Then $y = 2x$ models this relationship. The graph is a line through the origin.	Chicken costs $4.50 for the first pound, with a mimimum purchase of one pound, and $2 for each additional pound. Let y = number of dollars. Let x = number of pounds. Then $y = 2x + 2.50$ for $x \geq 1$ models this relationship. The graph is a line not through the origin.
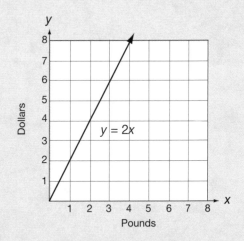	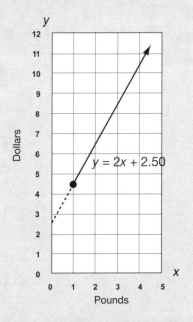
You can write many proportions for this relationship; one proportion is $$\frac{2 \text{ dollars}}{1 \text{ pound}} = \frac{8 \text{ dollars}}{4 \text{ pounds}}.$$ The unit rate (unit cost) is $\frac{2 \text{ dollars}}{1 \text{ pound}}$, or 2 dollars per pound, and 2 is the constant of proportionality. In other words, no matter how many pounds of chicken you buy in this situation, the cost per pound is constant.	This is not a proportional relationship. and therefore it involves no constant of proportionality. In other words, when you buy different numbers of pounds of chicken in this situation, the cost per pound varies.

Fig. 2.7. Comparing a proportional relationship and a relationship that is not proportional

- $y = 3x^2 + 1$ (a quadratic relationship)
- $y = 2^x$ (an exponential relationship)
- $y = 5 \cdot \dfrac{1}{x}$ (an inversely varying relationship)

Fig. 2.8. Examples of relationships that involve multiplication but are not proportional

Proportional Relationship				
$y = 2x$				
x	1	2	3	4
y	2	4	6	8
Ratio: $\dfrac{y}{x}$	$\dfrac{2}{1}$	$\dfrac{4}{2}$	$\dfrac{6}{3}$	$\dfrac{8}{4}$
Ratio in $r/1$ form	$\dfrac{2}{1}$	$\dfrac{2}{1}$	$\dfrac{2}{1}$	$\dfrac{2}{1}$

The constant of proportionality is 2.

Relationship That Is Not Proportional				
$y = 2x + 2.50$				
x	1	2	3	4
y	4.50	6.50	8.50	10.50
Ratio: $\dfrac{y}{x}$	$\dfrac{4.5}{1}$	$\dfrac{6.5}{2}$	$\dfrac{8.5}{3}$	$\dfrac{10.5}{4}$
Ratio in $r/1$ form	$\dfrac{4.5}{1}$	$\dfrac{3.25}{1}$	$\dfrac{2.8\overline{3}}{1}$	$\dfrac{2.625}{1}$

No constant of proportionality is involved.

Fig. 2.9. Example illustrating equivalent ratios and a constant of proportionality in a proportional relationship but not in a relationship that is not proportional

Developing proportional reasoning

Students have used proportional reasoning to solve problems prior to their formal study of proportionality. Thus, they should be encouraged to use representations related to their previous understandings as they learn about the properties of proportionality, as illustrated in the following classroom discussion of this problem:

If the cost of trading cards is two packs for $6, how much will it cost to buy 10 packages?

Teacher: As I was walking around, I saw that you used different methods to find the answer. Larry, can you explain how you solved the problem?

Larry: Sure. I knew that if I could figure out the cost of 1 package, then I could use multiplication to find the cost of 10 packages. You can buy 2 packages for $6, so you can divide both 2 and 6 by 2 to find that you can buy 1 package for $3. And, since you can buy 1 package for $3, the cost of 10 packages is 10 × $3, or $30.

The teacher should realize that Larry's representation includes an important and useful concept—unit rate. Unit rate plays an important role in proportionality because it can be used to connect students' intuitive understandings of proportionality to an understanding of constant of proportionality, or scale factor.

Teacher: Interesting approach, Larry. Maura, I noticed that you used a table as part of your solution process. Can you show your table and explain how you used it to solve the problem?

Maura: Here is the table that I made.

Number of Packages	2	4	6	8	10
Cost	6	12	18	24	30

I filled in a column to show 2 packages for $6. Then I used the same ratio over and over again to fill in more columns until I had the column with 10 packages. That column shows the answer. It would cost $30 to buy 10 packages.

The teacher notes that Maura made a ratio table. Ratio tables are important tools for understanding proportionality because they highlight an important characteristic of proportional relationships. The pairs of numbers in the table form equivalent ratios. Each pair of numbers in the table has the same multiplicative relationship, that is, the *x*-value (top row in Maura's table) is multiplied by the same number to get the *y*-value (bottom row in Maura's table).

Teacher: I understand. Amy, I noticed that your method of solving the problem was different than Larry's or Maura's. Can you explain your method?

Amy: I used ratios. I figured that the ratio of $6 to 2 packages must be equal to the ratio of the unknown cost to 10 packages. I wrote it like this:

$$\frac{\$6}{2 \text{ packages}} = \frac{x}{10 \text{ packages}}.$$

Then I realized that I needed to multiply 2 by 5 to get 10, so I multiplied 6 by 5 to get 30. So the cost of 10 packages is $30.

Amy used what she knew about equivalent ratios to solve the problem. The teacher should realize that without using proportionality language, Amy used a pair of equivalent ratios to represent a proportion to solve the problem. Referring to the classroom discussion, the teacher now has an opportunity to introduce some useful representations that will help students connect the representations they have created from their current understanding to more formal representations of proportionality, as illustrated in the continuation of the classroom discussion.

Teacher: Larry, Maura, and Amy all used different methods to find the solution to the problem, yet all their methods included multiplication and division. We can link these methods by using a strip model. We need to compare $6 to 2 packages.

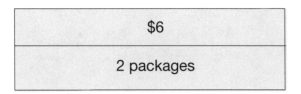

$6
2 packages

Then we need to repeat the model of the comparison enough times so that we end up with 10 packages. What operation can we use to represent what we are doing? [multiplication]

$30				
$6	$6	$6	$6	$6
2 packages	2 packages	2 packages	2 packages	2 packages
10 packages				

Strip models can also be used to show scaling down, for example, if you are given that 10 packages cost $30 and you need to find the cost of 2 packages. (Scaling up can be accomplished by multiplication; scaling down can be accomplished by division.) The strip model is a powerful representation because it can be applied in a wide variety of proportional situations. Once students understand how their models are related and how they can use a strip model to represent the relationships in the problem, the teacher can connect students' understanding of the problem to proportionality, as shown in the continued classroom discussion that follows.

Teacher: Let's use the strip model to make a table. The first strip shows that the cost of 2 packages is $6. Record this relationship in the first column of the table. Two of these strips show that 4 packages cost $12. Record this relationship in the second column of the table. Continue using the strips to record the relationships.

Cost	6	12	18	24	30
Number of Packages	2	4	6	8	10

The number pairs shown in the table, that is, 2 packages for $6, 4 packages for $12, 6 packages for $18, and so on, can be written as equivalent ratios:

$$\frac{\$6}{2 \text{ packages}} = \frac{\$12}{4 \text{ packages}} = \frac{\$18}{6 \text{ packages}}.$$

We say that there is a constant ratio between dollars and packages, so the relationship between dollars and packages in this problem is *proportional*. If we divide 6 and 2 in the ratio

$$\frac{\$6}{2 \text{ packages}}$$

by 2, we get the equivalent ratio

$$\frac{\$3}{1 \text{ package}}, \frac{\$6}{2 \text{ packages}}, \frac{\$30}{10 \text{ packages}}.$$

which is the *unit rate* in this situation. We can also use strips to show this relationship.

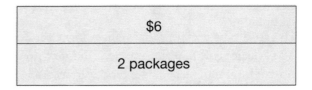

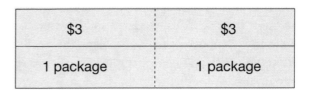

Any two ratios represented in the table are equivalent ratios. To indicate their equivalence, we write, for example,

$$\frac{\$6}{2 \text{ packages}} = \frac{\$30}{10 \text{ packages}}.$$

An equation that expresses the equivalence of two ratios is a proportion.

Once students are able to connect their prior understandings to the concept of proportions, teachers can then show students how to solve the same problem by writing a proportion with a missing value and then finding that missing value. For example, in the previous classroom discussion, a teacher might continue as follows.

Teacher: When Amy represented the relationships in the problem using equivalent ratios,

$$\frac{\$6}{2 \text{ packages}} = \frac{x}{10 \text{ packages}},$$

she was actually writing a proportion. Since there is a constant multiplicative relationship between the number of packages and the number of dollars, you can use a proportion to represent that relationship. Then you can solve the proportion by finding the unknown value.

Reflect As You Read

How might you help students connect their own procedures for determining the missing value in this proportion to the use of a generally applicable procedure, such as cross multiplication? How might you explain to your students *why* cross multiplication works?

One of the teacher's tasks during instruction is to introduce representations that help students connect their informal representations of proportionality to the desired formal representations, for example, writing a proportion. Classroom discussions such as the previous ones help teachers determine the understandings that students bring to the discussion of proportionality. For example, students may create their own ratio table or use the equivalent ratios method to represent proportionality on the basis of what they already know. For other students, it might be necessary for the teacher to introduce the idea of a ratio table or the use of equivalent ratios. Regardless of the level of understanding that each student brings, the teacher needs to introduce the appropriate representations that will guide the student through the connection of prior experiences with proportionality to a more formal representation of a proportion. An understanding of the formal representation of a proportion provides students with an efficient and effective way to solve problems involving proportionality.

Solving for a missing value in a proportion

As a result of building understanding of proportionality, students should be able to recognize a proportional relationship in a problem, set up a proportion with a missing value that can be used to solve the problem, and use an efficient method to find the missing value, as shown in figure 2.10.

For students to apply these techniques effectively, it is important that they have a solid understanding of proportionality and an understanding of why the *cross multiplication* procedure works. Teachers want to ensure that students build this algorithmic procedure from a strong mathematical foundation so that they can transfer its use to other appropriate situations and do not try to use it in inappropriate situations.

Problem: Janie is reading a 32-page chapter of a book. She read 6 pages in 15 minutes. If she continues to read at the same rate, how long will it take her to read the entire chapter?

Solution:

$$\frac{6}{15} = \frac{32}{x}$$

$$6x = 15 \cdot 32$$

$$6x = 480$$

$$x = 80$$

It will take Janie 80 minutes to read the entire chapter.

Fig. 2.10. Example of a proportionality problem and a solution

Once students feel comfortable with using proportions to represent proportional situations, they can use several methods to find a missing value in the proportion. In initial explorations of solving proportions, students will draw on their ability to form equivalent fractions and ratios to solve for a missing value in a proportion. Examples of this method are shown in figure 2.11.

Solve $\dfrac{2}{3} = \dfrac{x}{12}$.

Solution:

$$\frac{2}{3} = \frac{x}{12}$$ ⟵ Think, "3 times what number equals 12?"

$$\frac{2 \times 4}{3 \times 4} = \frac{8}{12}$$ Reason, "3 times 4 equals 12, so to form equivalent ratios, I need to multiply 2 by 4 to find the unknown numerator."

So $x = 8$.

Solve $\dfrac{15}{18} = \dfrac{5}{x}$.

Solution:

$$\frac{15}{18} = \frac{5}{x}$$ ⟵ Think, "15 divided by what number equals 5?"

$$\frac{15 \div 3}{18 \div 3} = \frac{5}{6}$$ Reason, "15 divided by 3 equals 5, so to form equivalent ratios, I need to divide 18 by 3 to find the unknown denominator."

So $x = 6$.

Fig. 2.11. Using equivalent ratios to find missing values in proportions

With carefully crafted examples, however, students quickly realize that this method is not easy to apply to all proportions. Consider the example in figure 2.12.

Solve $\dfrac{6}{9} = \dfrac{x}{6}$.

$\dfrac{6}{9} = \dfrac{x}{6}$ ←——— Think, "9 divided by what number equals 6?"

There is not a whole number that will do this.

This method is not as easy to use for this proportion.

Fig. 2.12. Example that illustrates the limitations of the "form an equivalent ratio" method of finding the missing value in a proportion

With an increase in the sophistication of the problems that students solve, they become aware that they need another method, other than the equivalent ratio method, to find a missing value in a proportion. Thus, a reason for teachers to introduce another method for finding a missing value in a proportion arises.

Cross multiplication or *finding the cross product* is a method that is efficient and commonly used to solve for an unknown value in a proportion. As previously stated, however, it is important that teachers and students understand why the cross-product method works. To build students' understanding of the method of cross multiplying to find a missing value in a proportion, teachers should start with students' understanding of equivalent fractions, for example, 6/9 and 4/6. Prior to grade 7, students have used common denominators as one way to verify that two fractions are equivalent. They have learned that when equivalent fractions that look different are rewritten with the same denominators, their numerators are then also the same. So to show that 6/9 is equivalent to 4/6, students can rewrite the fractions with a common denominator. One obvious common denominator they can use is the product of the two denominators, $9 \times 6 = 54$. To write 6/9 and 4/6 as equivalent fractions with denominator 54, they can use the procedure shown in figure 2.13.

As students can see from their work in figure 2.13, when 6/9 and 4/6 are written as fractions with a denominator of 54, they are both equivalent to 36/54, so they are equivalent fractions. Students can build on this foundational understanding of equivalent fractions and the understanding of ratios represented as fractions to find a missing numerator or denominator that will make two ratios equivalent, as shown in figure 2.14.

$$\frac{6}{9} = \frac{6 \times 6}{9 \times 6} = \frac{36}{54}$$

Write each fraction as an equivalent fraction that has 54 as its denominator.

$$\frac{4}{6} = \frac{4 \times 9}{6 \times 9} = \frac{36}{54}$$

$$\frac{6}{9} = \frac{4}{6}$$

Because $\frac{6}{9}$ and $\frac{4}{6}$ are both equivalent to $\frac{36}{54}$, they are equivalent to each other by the transitive property of equality.

Fig. 2.13. Using common denominators to verify that two fractions are equivalent

Find the value of x that makes $\frac{6}{9} = \frac{x}{6}$ true.

$$\frac{6}{9} = \frac{x}{6}$$

$$\frac{6 \cdot 6}{9 \cdot 6} = \frac{x \cdot 9}{6 \cdot 9}$$

Write each fraction as an equivalent fraction that has 54 as its denominator.

$$\frac{36}{54} = \frac{9x}{54}$$

Because $\frac{36}{54}$ is equivalent to $\frac{9x}{54}$, 36 must be equal to 9x,

$$\frac{36}{54} = \frac{9 \cdot 4}{54}$$

and x = 4.

So, x = 4.

Fig. 2.14. Finding equivalent ratios by using common denominators

Once students develop a conceptual understanding behind the procedure in figure 2.14, teachers can connect this understanding to proportions. They can point out that

$$\frac{6}{9} = \frac{x}{6}$$

is a proportion with a missing value and that, by using the procedure in figure 2.14, they have found the value of x that solves the proportion.

After completing various examples such as the one in figure 2.14, students will begin to realize that in every instance, once they have used the products of the denominators as a common denominator to translate the two fractions into equivalent forms, they need only to find the number that makes the numerators equivalent and can disregard the denominators. On further analysis, they should realize that this procedure is the same as multiplying the numerator of one ratio by the denominator of the other ratio and setting it equal to the product of the denominator of the first ratio and the numerator of the other ratio, as illustrated in figure 2.15. Thus, the cross-product method is a shortcut for representing the numerators when the original ratios are written as equivalent ratios with the products of the original denominators as the common denominator of the new ratios.

$$\frac{6}{9} = \frac{x}{6}$$

$$\frac{6 \cdot 6}{9 \cdot 6} = \frac{x \cdot 9}{6 \cdot 9}$$

$$\frac{36}{54} = \frac{9x}{54}$$

$$\frac{36}{54} = \frac{9 \cdot 4}{54}$$

So $x = 4$.

$$\frac{6}{9} = \frac{x}{6}$$

$$6 \cdot 6 = x \cdot 9$$

$$36 = 9x$$

$$36 = 9 \cdot 4$$

So $x = 4$.

Fig. 2.15. Example illustrating the cross-product method as a short-cut for representing the numerators of equivalent ratios with common denominators

Specifically, since

$$\frac{6}{9} = \frac{6 \cdot 6}{9 \cdot 6} = \frac{36}{54}$$

and

$$\frac{x}{6} = \frac{x \cdot 9}{6 \cdot 9} = \frac{9x}{54},$$

the original equation can be replaced by the equivalent equation,

$$\frac{36}{54} = \frac{9x}{54}.$$

But two fractions are equal if and only if their numerators are equal, so this equation is solved by solving the equation formed by setting the two numerators equal, that is, by solving $36 = 9x$. Dividing each side of this equation by 9 identifies the solution $x = 4$.

This relationship can also be shown algebraically and can be applied to any proportion $a/b = c/d$ where $b \neq 0$ and $d \neq 0$, as shown in figure 2.16.

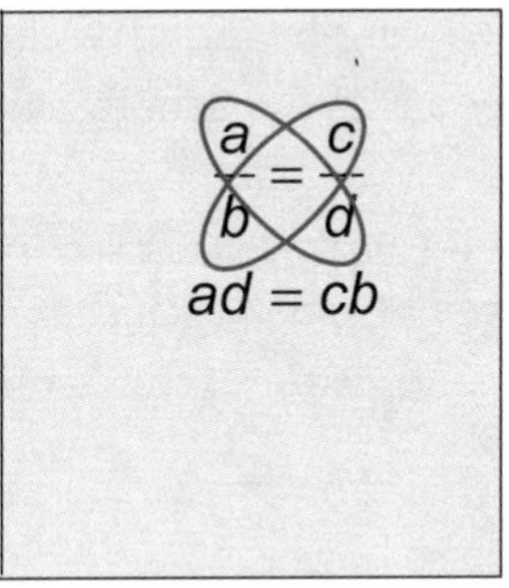

Fig. 2.16. Algebraic representation of the cross-product method

Once students have gained a conceptual understanding of the cross-product method and can use it meaningfully to find missing values in proportions, teachers can revisit previously solved problems and show students how they can solve these problems and similar problems by using cross products, as is illustrated in the classroom discussion that follows.

Teacher: Remember the problem in which you buy 2 packages of trading cards for $6 and you want to find out how much it would cost to buy 10 packages? We discovered that we could use proportionality to represent this problem. We wrote the proportion

$$\frac{6}{2} = \frac{x}{10}.$$

We found that the answer to this problem was $30. Can anyone tell me how we could have used cross products to find the answer?

Michelle: I think I can. If I write the equivalent ratios as equivalent fractions with 2 × 10 as the denominator of the new fractions, I would write

$$\frac{6 \cdot 10}{2 \cdot 10} = \frac{x \cdot 2}{10 \cdot 2}$$

$$\frac{60}{20} = \frac{2x}{20}.$$

Then I would find the value of x that would make $2x$ equal to 60. But I know now that the shortcut way of getting the numerators is to cross multiply, so I can cross multiply and solve for x:

$$\frac{6}{2} \diagdown \frac{x}{10}$$

$$6 \times 10 = 2x$$
$$60 = 2x$$
$$30 = x$$

Teacher: You applied cross products correctly, Michelle. But why would we need to learn how to solve this problem using cross products when we already know the answer? Consider this problem: You buy 10 packages of trading cards for $8. How much would it cost to buy 24 packages? This is the same type of problem as we just solved. What proportion can we write to represent this problem?

Jeff: The problem says you spend $8 for 10 cards and an unknown amount of dollars for 24 cards, so I can write

$$\frac{8}{10} = \frac{x}{24}.$$

Teacher: Look at Jeff's proportion. It is not as easy now to make equivalent ratios by finding a number times 10 that makes 24. Can anyone tell me how they could use what they have learned about common denominators to solve this problem?

Chas: Yes, I see how to find the answer! I can use cross products to find the numerators if the common denominator was 10 × 24:

$$\frac{8}{10} \diagdown \frac{x}{24}$$

$$8 \times 24 = 10x$$
$$192 = 10x$$
$$19.2 = x$$

So 24 packages cost $19.20.

As students solve various problems such as the ones in the previous classroom discussion, they will begin to appreciate the power of using proportions and cross products to represent and solve problems involving proportionality. By connecting the application of cross products to the creation of equal ratios in a proportion, students may avoid common misapplications of cross products (e.g, when adding, subtracting, or multiplying two fractions).

Strengthening Understanding of Proportionality through Problem Solving

It is important that students solve proportionality problems that include a variety of contexts and types. Some important types of problems include missing value, numerical comparison, qualitative comparison, and qualitative prediction. Teachers can read about these kinds of problems in *Navigating through Number and Operations* (Rachlin et al. 2006). Problem-solving experiences should also be carefully constructed to help students contrast proportional relationships and relationships that are not proportional. Teachers should also present problems that help students understand how to apply proportionality to solve problems related to different topics in mathematics, such as similarity, slope, and percent.

Problems that contrast proportional relationships and relationships that are not proportional

To help students learn to distinguish proportional relationships from relationships that are not proportional, teachers should present students with pairs of problems that use the same context but in which the relationship in one problem is proportional and the relationship in the other problem is not proportional. After students have solved the problems, they can learn how to compare their solution methods and their dependence on the characteristics of proportional relationships and relationships that are not proportional. Those characteristics are identifiable in graphs and tables, so teachers should help students revise or supplement their solution methods as needed to incorporate graphs and tables. Pairs of problems, such as the ones shown in figure 2.17, can help solidify students' understanding of proportionality.

Although all the points on the graphs in each of the problems in figure 2.17 lie on a straight line, the problems involve discrete data, not continuous data, so dotted lines rather than solid lines should be used. Furthermore, the lines on the path in the graph in problem 1 lie on a straight path through the origin; therefore the graph represents a proportional relationship.

After students have solved these problems, teachers should have students compare the data found in the tables as well as compare the graphs. As students develop their understanding, they will begin to realize that in problem 1, the related *x*- and *y*-values in the table create equivalent ratios:

$$\frac{y}{x} = \frac{\text{number of cents}}{\text{number of meters}} = \frac{40}{50} = \frac{80}{100} = \ldots = \frac{4}{5}$$

and that every *y/x* ratio is equivalent to 4/5. In problem 2, no such constant ratio exists. Students, then, begin to identify the relationship in problem 1 as proportional and the relationship in problem 2 as not proportional.

As students analyze the graphs of the relationships, they should realize that the points on the graph of the relationship in problem 1 are contained in a line that passes through the origin; the points on the graph of the relationship in problem 2 are also contained in a line, but it does not pass through the origin. Again, after many experiences with similar pairs of problems, students will begin to recognize the graph of a proportional relationship as a line that passes through the origin, and that any other type of graph (either nonlinear or a line not passing through the origin) indicates a relationship that is not proportional.

Problem 1: Ray is participating in a fund-raiser at his swim club. He is signing up people to pledge donations based on how many 50-meter laps he swims. His first pledge agrees to donate $0.40 for every 50 meters he swims. If Ray swims 400 meters, how much will he earn from that pledge? Set up a table, and make a graph as you solve the problem.

Solution:

Meters (x)	50	100	150	200	250	300	350	400	450	500
Cents (y)	40	80	120	160	200	240	280	320	360	400

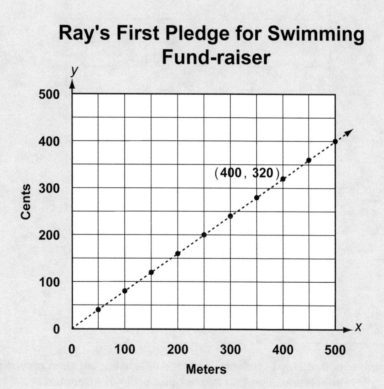

Ray will earn 320 cents, or $3.20, from his first pledge.

(Continued on next page)

Fig. 2.17. Pair of problems that helps students learn the difference between proportional relationships and relationships that are not proportional

Problem 2: Amanda is participating in the same fund-raiser. Her first pledge agrees to donate $1.00, plus $0.30 for every 50 meters she swims. If Amanda swims 400 meters, how much will she earn from that pledge? Set up a table, and make a graph as you solve the problem.

Solution:

Meters (x)	50	100	150	200	250	300	350	400	450	500
Cents (y)	130	160	190	220	250	280	310	340	370	400

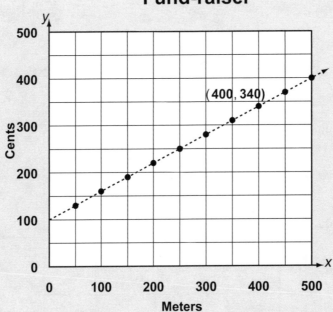

Amanda's First Pledge for Swimming Fund-raiser

Amanda will earn 340 cents, or $3.40, from her first pledge.

Fig. 2.17. Pair of problems that helps students learn the difference between proportional relationships and relationships that are not proportional—Continued

Similar geometric figures

Among many important proportionality problems that students will encounter are problems involving similar geometric figures. These problems will include the most familiar type—finding measures of sides of similar polygons—and might also involve applications in other contexts, such as maps, scale drawings, and three-dimensional scale models. In these contexts, the constant of proportionality is often called the *scale factor*. When a figure "grows," the constant of proportionality, or scale factor, k, is greater than 1. When the figure "shrinks," *k* is less than 1 but greater than 0, and if the figure stays the same, *k* is equal to 1. In that situation, the first figure is the same size and shape as, or *congruent to,* the second figure. Congruence is one type of similarity.

Students should first be presented with similar figures with measures of all sides and angles given. Students should learn that for two figures to be similar, all pairs of corresponding angles are congruent and all pairs of corresponding lengths are proportional (form the same ratio). Therefore, in similar figures, the length of any side of one figure times the constant of proportionality, or scale factor, *k,* is equal to the corresponding length of the other figure, and the ratio of any two lengths in one figure is equal to the ratio of the corresponding lengths in a similar figure. These properties are illustrated in the example in figure 2.18.

After students have had many opportunities to analyze the relationships in similar figures, they can use what they have observed to solve problems involving similar figures, for example, problems in which side lengths are not known, as illustrated in figure 2.19. Note that understanding of efficient solution strategies for these problems is dependent on previously developed understanding of the properties of proportionality and similarity and the connection of cross multiplication to the creation of equivalent ratios.

Slope

Graphs of proportional relationships can be used to introduce the idea of the slope of a line. A problem-solving situation involving proportionality, such as the one shown in figure 2.20, provides a purposeful opportunity for students to learn that the ratio of the change in *y* to the change in *x* between any two points on a line graph is constant and that this constant ratio, or constant rate of change, is called the *slope of the line.*

As shown in figure 2.21, teachers can help students use their graphs to see that the change in *y* is proportional to the change in *x* because the ratio of the change in *y* to the change in *x* has the constant value 2, regardless of which two points on the line are used. Then teachers can point out that this constant ratio, 2/1 or 2, represents the slope of this line. Students should be guided to notice that the slope of the line representing the proportional relationship between minutes and pictures printed is equal to the constant of proportionality in the relationship, and they should be encouraged to test this out on other graphs of proportional relationships. In later grades students will extend their exploration of slope to include linear relationships that are not proportional and will use slope to solve problems.

Percent

In their work with rational numbers in grade 7 students learn to represent percents with fractions and decimals. Since fractions can be used to represent ratios, and percents are ratios, then fractions and their equivalent decimal forms can be used to represent percents. For example, students learn that a percent is a ratio of a part of 100 to the total of 100. For example, 50 percent

If figure A is similar to figure B, then:

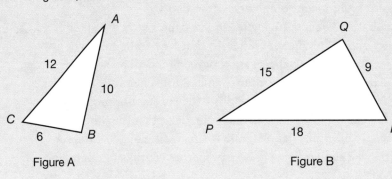

Figure A   Figure B

- $\angle A \cong \angle P, \angle B \cong \angle Q, \angle C \cong \angle R.$
- Pairs of corresponding lengths are proportional: $\dfrac{12}{18} = \dfrac{6}{9} = \dfrac{10}{15}$, and the constant of proportionality, or scale factor, k, is the simplest form of these ratios: $\dfrac{2}{3}$.
- You can multiply the dimensions in figure B by the scale factor, $k = \dfrac{2}{3}$, to obtain the dimensions in figure A, that is:

$$y = kx$$
$$y = \frac{2}{3}x$$
$$y = \frac{2}{3}(15)$$
$$y = \frac{30}{3}$$
$$y = 10$$

- Any two ratios of corresponding dimensions can be used to write a proportion, for example, $\dfrac{12}{18} = \dfrac{10}{15}$.
- The ratio of any two lengths in figure A is equal to the ratio of the corresponding lengths in figure B: $\dfrac{10}{12} = \dfrac{15}{18}$, $\dfrac{10}{6} = \dfrac{15}{9}$, and $\dfrac{6}{12} = \dfrac{9}{18}$.

Fig. 2.18. Proportional relationships in similar triangles

means 50 out of 100, or 50/100. Because percents are ratios, students can use proportionality to solve problems involving percent, including problems involving discounts, interest, taxes, tips, and percent of increase and decrease. In initial experiences, students should use strip diagrams, or percent bar representations, to model percents. Percent bar representations, such as the one shown in figure 2.22, can help students understand percents conceptually and get a sense of a reasonable answer. Using the bar model makes it easier for students to set up the correct proportion.

Problem: $\triangle ABC$ and $\triangle PQR$ are similar. Find the length of $\overline{QR}$.

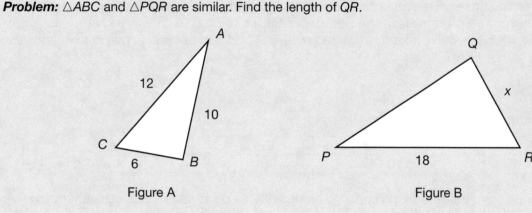

Figure A   Figure B

Solution 1: All corresponding lengths in similar figures are proportional, so $\dfrac{12}{18} = \dfrac{6}{x}$.

$$\frac{12}{18} = \frac{6}{x}$$
$$12x = 18 \cdot 6$$
$$12x = 108$$
$$x = 9$$

The missing side has a length of 9 units.

Solution 2: The ratio of any two lengths in one figure is equal to the ratio of the corresponding lengths in a similar figure, so $\dfrac{6}{12} = \dfrac{x}{18}$.

$$\frac{6}{12} = \frac{x}{18}$$
$$6 \cdot 18 = 12x$$
$$108 = 12x$$
$$9 = x$$

The missing side has a length of 9 units.

Fig. 2.19. Using properties of similarity to find the length of a side of a triangle

Percent problems are often described as falling into one of three categories—finding part of a whole, finding a percent, and finding the whole when given the percent. Some students have difficulty determining into which of these categories a problem fits, and consequently they are unsure about how to solve the problem. But all three types of problems can be solved by beginning with the same generic proportion, and learning this strategy helps many students avoid the uncertainty. The following generic proportion can be used to solve all three types of percent problems:

Problem: You have 36 pictures to print for your scrapbook. In 5 minutes, your printer prints 10 pictures. If the printer continues to print at the same rate, how many minutes will it take to print 36 pictures? Use a table and a graph to illustrate your solution.

Solution: Make a table.

Minutes (x)	5	10	15	?	20
Pictures (y)	10	20	30	36	40

Use any pair of numbers from the table along with 36 pictures and its corresponding unknown number of minutes to write a proportion and solve.

$$\frac{5}{10} = \frac{x}{36}$$
$$5 \cdot 36 = 10x$$
$$180 = 10x$$
$$18 = x$$

It will take 18 minutes to print 36 pictures.

Use the table to make a graph.

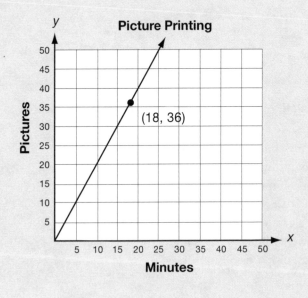

Fig. 2.20. Example of a problem that can be used to introduce the concept of slope

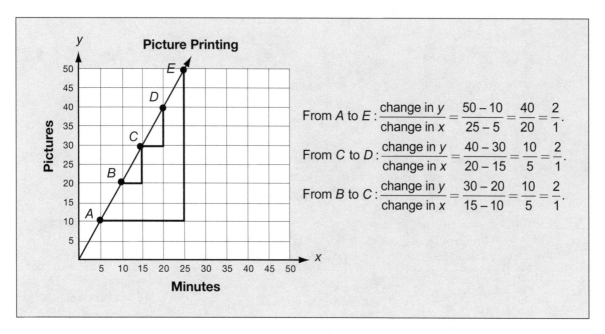

Fig. 2.21. Example illustrating the proportionality of slope

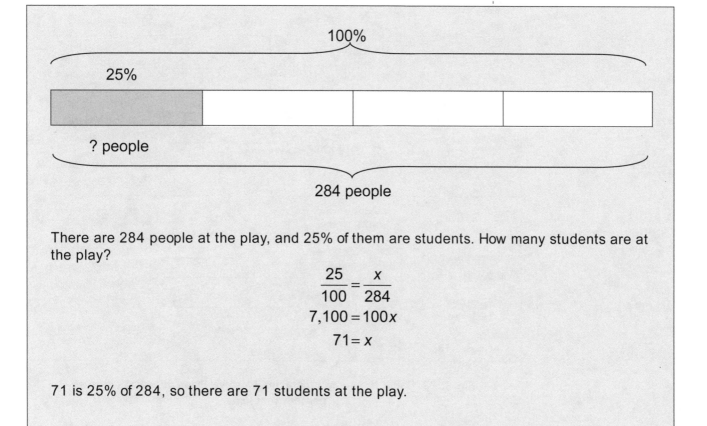

There are 284 people at the play, and 25% of them are students. How many students are at the play?

$$\frac{25}{100} = \frac{x}{284}$$
$$7{,}100 = 100x$$
$$71 = x$$

71 is 25% of 284, so there are 71 students at the play.

Fig. 2.22. Example showing how to use a percent bar representation

$$\frac{\text{part}}{\text{whole}} = \frac{p}{100},$$

where

$$\frac{p}{100}$$

is the fractional form of the ratio representing the percent ($p\%$). Figure 2.23 shows the three types of percent questions, a percent bar diagram, and a solved example for each type.

Problem Type ($p\%$ of whole = part)	Example	Bar Diagram	Solution
Finding part of a whole: 40% of $25 = *part*.	The regular price of a skirt is $25. The skirt is on sale for 40% off. What is the savings?	100% 40% *s* dollars $25	$\frac{\text{part}}{\text{whole}} = \frac{p}{100}$ $\frac{s}{25} = \frac{40}{100}$ $100s = 25 \cdot 40$ $100s = 1000$ $s = 10$ The savings is $10.
Finding a percent: $p\%$ of $25 = $10.	The regular price of a skirt is $25. The skirt is on sale for $10 off. What percent of the regular price is the savings?	100% *p*% $10 $25	$\frac{\text{part}}{\text{whole}} = \frac{p}{100}$ $\frac{10}{25} = \frac{p}{100}$ $25p = 10 \cdot 100$ $25p = 1000$ $p = 40$ The savings is 40% of the regular price.
Finding the whole: 40% of *whole* = $10.	A skirt is on sale for 40% off. With the sale you save $10. What is the regular price of the skirt?	100% 40% $10 *r* dollars	$\frac{\text{part}}{\text{whole}} = \frac{p}{100}$ $\frac{10}{r} = \frac{40}{100}$ $40r = 10 \cdot 100$ $40r = 1000$ $r = 25$ The regular price is $25.

Fig. 2.23. Using the same proportion to solve three different types of percent problems

Students can also apply their understanding of proportionality and percent to problems involving circle graphs. Two sample problems are shown in figure 2.24.

38

Problem 1: A group of 80 students voted to choose a seventh-grade team name for Sports Day. The results are shown in the table. Mariah, the class president, is making a circle graph to represent the results. What is the angle measure that corresponds to the sector of the circle that goes with Raiders?

Solution:

$$\frac{12}{80} = \frac{x}{360}$$

$$80x = 12 \cdot 360$$

$$80x = 4,320$$

$$x = 54$$

Name	Votes
Panthers	16
Bears	20
Raiders	12
Comets	32

The sector for Raiders is 54 degrees.

Problem 2: Mariah made the circle graph to show the results of the Sports Day name survey from problem 1. What percent of the students voted for Raiders as the team name?

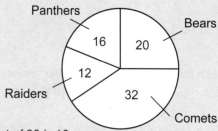

Solution: Find what percent of 80 is 12.

$$\frac{\text{part}}{\text{whole}} = \frac{p}{100}$$

$$\frac{12}{80} = \frac{p}{100}$$

$$80p = 12 \cdot 100$$

$$80p = 1200$$

$$p = 15$$

15 percent of the students voted for Raiders as the team name.

Fig. 2.24. Using proportionality and percent to solve problems involving circle graphs

Strengthening Understanding through Connections

As students become aware of connections among mathematical concepts, they gain a more thorough understanding of the concepts. Becoming aware of how proportions are used in different mathematical topics will help students deepen their understanding of proportionality. Students can connect their developing proportional reasoning skills to contexts involving measurement, circles, data analysis, and probability.

Students learn that they can use proportionality to convert from one unit of measure to another, as shown in figure 2.25. The conversion factor is the same as a scale factor.

Problem: How many inches are in 5 feet?

Solution:

$$\frac{\text{number of inches}}{\text{number of feet}} = \frac{12}{1}$$

$$\frac{x}{5} = \frac{12}{1}$$

$$1x = 5 \cdot 12$$

$$x = 60$$

There are 60 inches in 5 feet.

Fig. 2.25. Example showing how to use proportions to convert between units of measure

The proportional relationships involved in similarity are also the basic concepts underlying the formulas for circumference and area of circles. Because all circles are similar to one another, the ratios of the circumference (C) of any circle to the diameter (d) of that circle are equivalent to one another. It is known that the common ratio of the circumference of any circle to its diameter is an irrational number; that is, this ratio is not rational because it cannot be expressed as a repeating or terminating decimal. To make it easier to write the value of this ratio and use it in computations, it is represented by π (the Greek letter pi). Initial experiences with π should have students using string or pipe cleaners to measure the circumferences and diameters of circles and recording and analyzing the approximate relationships of the measurements, as illustrated in the problem in figure 2.26, so that students can begin to understand the proportional relationship of the circumference to the diameter.

Teachers should make sure that students understand that π is a number whose decimal notation does not terminate or repeat (3.14159265…) and that the values commonly used for π (3.14 and 22/7) are just estimates of that number used in computation, just as we might use 2 for 2.2 to estimate a product or quotient.

Teachers can lead students to connect their understandings of proportionality and its algebraic representations to determine how to find the circumference of a circle when given its diameter (or radius):

Circumference of a Circle

Problem: Use string to measure around each circle. Then place the length of string over the diameter of the circle to see how many diameters you can make from the string.

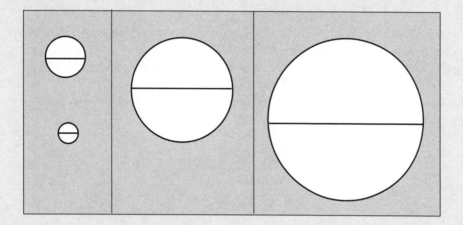

Solution:

You can make a little more than 3 diameters out of each circumference-length string, that is, $C \approx 3(d)$ or

$$\frac{C}{d} \approx \frac{3}{1}$$

Fig. 2.26. An experience that explores the constant ratio between the circumference of a circle and its diameter

$$\frac{C}{d} = \frac{\pi}{1}$$
$$C \cdot 1 = \pi d$$
$$C = \pi d$$

Note that this equation is in the form $y = kx$, where $y = C$, $k = \pi$, and $x = d$. Therefore the equation indicates that π is the constant of proportionality in this relationship. Additionally, since a diameter is made up of two radii, $d = 2r$, substitution produces an equivalent equation, $C = 2\pi r$. Students can then use their understanding of this formula to solve problems involving the circumference, diameter, or radius of a circle.

Once students understand π as the number that describes the constant ratio of circumference to diameter, they can begin to consider its use in the formula for the area of a circle. It requires the use of calculus to derive formally the formula for the area of circles in later grades, but students in grade

7 should encounter representations that help build intuitive understanding of the formula for the area of a circle: $A = \pi r^2$.

Proportionality is often used in data analysis. In the sample problem shown in figure 2.27, proportionality is used to make an estimate about a population from a sample of the population.

Problem: A representative sample of 200 voters is chosen to be surveyed from 5,400 people who voted in an election of a town mayor. Pollsters use this technique of sampling a portion of the population to make a prediction about the whole group without asking everyone. Of the 200 voters surveyed, 85 said they voted for candidate X. Use the result of the survey to estimate how many of the 5,400 votes you would expect candidate X to receive in the election.

Solution:

$$\frac{x}{5,400} = \frac{85}{200}$$

$$200x = 85 \cdot 5,400$$

$$200x = 459,000$$

$$x = 2,295$$

On the basis of the survey, we would expect candidate X to receive close to 2,295 votes in the election.

Fig. 2.27. Using proportionality in data analysis

Since a probability is a ratio of the number of favorable outcomes to the number of all possible outcomes, students can use their understanding of proportionality to solve problems involving probability. In the sample problem in figure 2.28, a proportion is used to determine the number of marbles in a jar.

Connections in later grades

Understanding and applying proportional reasoning will be necessary for students to be successful in many of the topics they will encounter in later grades, both in mathematics and in other subject areas, such as chemistry and economics. In later grades, students will connect the term *direct variation* to proportional relationships in the form $y = kx$. They will contrast direct variations with indirect variations that are represented by $y \cdot x = k$. Students will apply proportionality to solve problems involving side lengths, perimeters, areas, and volumes of similar objects. They will apply proportionality to solve problems involving parallel lines cut by transversals, intersecting chords of a circle, and the altitude to the hypotenuse of a right triangle.

Students will need to understand the relationship of a line's slope to the similar triangles formed by using segments on the line as sides of the triangles and the related "rise" and "run" segments as the other sides. They will learn the definition of slope as the ratio of rise to run, along with other equivalent

Sample Problem: The probability of choosing a blue marble from a jar of 100 marbles is $\frac{3}{5}$. How many marbles in the jar are blue?

Solution:

$$\frac{x}{100} = \frac{3}{5}$$
$$5x = 3 \cdot 100$$
$$5x = 300$$
$$x = 60$$

Sixty of the marbles in the jar are blue.

Fig. 2.28. A problem that shows the connection between proportionality and probability

definitions. They will use proportionality and the definition of slope to derive equations of lines; they will see that the point-slope form of the equation of a line is the direct result of the proportional relationship that exists between rise and run. In trigonometry, students will use proportionality as they apply the law of sines to find missing side lengths in triangles.

Developing Depth of Understanding

What activities and problems can you give students to help them learn the difference between proportional relationships and relationships that are not proportional? How can you help students deepen their understanding of proportionality by making connections between different representations of a proportional relationship, for example, equivalent ratios, ordered pairs in a table, linear equation, and graph of a line?

3 Focusing on Understanding Surface Area and Volume

In grade 7 students build understanding of the equations and formulas to compute surface area and volume. They become aware of the reasoning that underlies the derivation of the formulas, and they apply that reasoning to compute measurements. For example, they learn about several formulas for surface area but also learn that all the formulas are based on the same concept—that surface area is the sum of the areas of all the surfaces of the figure. Also, they learn about several formulas for volume of prisms and cylinders, but they also learn that all those formulas are also based on the same principle—for these solids, the volume is the product of the area of the base of the figure and its height. If students understand these concepts, they can apply the reasoning that underlies the derivation of a formula to reconstruct it. For the purposes of this grade 7 Focal Point, *prism* means *right prism* and *cylinder* means *right cylinder*. In future grades, students will work with oblique (or "leaning") prisms and cylinders.

Instructional Progression for Surface Area and Volume

The focus on surface area and volume in grade 7 is supported by a progression of related mathematical ideas before and after grade 7, as shown in table 3.1. To give perspective to the grade 7 work, we first discuss some of the important ideas that students focused on before grade 7 that prepare them for learning about surface area and volume in grade 7. At the end of the detailed discussion of this grade 7 Focal Point, we present examples of how students will use the surface area and volume understandings and skills in later grades. For more detailed discussions of the "before" and "after" parts of the instructional progression, please see the appropriate grade-level books, *Focus in Grade 3*, *Focus in Grade 4*, *Focus in Grade 5*, *Focus in Grade 6*, and *Focus in Grade 8*.

Table 3.1 represents an instructional progression for the conceptual understanding of surface area and volume before grade 7, during grade 7, and after grade 7.

Early Foundations for Understanding Surface Area and Volume

Before grade 7, students are exposed to a variety of skills and concepts that they can use to help them understand surface area and volume. For example, students analyze, classify, and decompose three-dimensional figures. Also, they work with perimeter and area of two-dimensional figures, including

Table 3.1
Grade 7: Focusing on Surface Area and Volume—Instructional Progression for Surface Area and Volume

Before Grade 7	Grade 7	After Grade 7
Students decompose familiar three-dimensional figures (e.g., cylinders, polyhedra, and cones) into their two-dimensional surfaces (i.e., nets). Students develop an understanding of the attributes of area, surface area, and volume and the types of units used to measure each of them. Students use area formulas for common polygons (e.g., triangle, rectangle, etc.) to solve problems. Students develop the skills to use expressions, equations, and formulas to solve problems (e.g., apply the understanding of equivalent expressions to decide between the use of $5x$ or $2x + 3x$ in the solution to a problem).	Students find surface area of prisms and cylinders by decomposing the three-dimensional shape into its two-dimensional components. Students derive and justify the formula for volume of prisms and cylinders (volume = area of base × height) by decomposing the three-dimensional shape into smaller component shapes. Students understand and are able to describe the relationship between the scale factor and the areas and volumes of similar figures. Students solve a variety of problems involving area, surface area, circumference of circles, and volume of prisms and cylinders using various strategies.	Students understand the relationships among the angle measures, side lengths, perimeters, areas, and volumes of similar objects and use these relationships to solve problems. Students develop an understanding of the Pythagorean theorem (i.e., given a right triangle, then the lengths of the sides have a specific relationship) and its converse (i.e., given the specific relationship between the lengths of the sides of a triangle, then the triangle must be a right triangle.). Students apply the Pythagorean theorem and its converse to solve problems.

circumference of circles. Students explore the volume of rectangular prisms. Finally, students use expressions, equations, and formulas to represent relationships.

Previously, students have analyzed certain three-dimensional figures. They distinguish polyhedra, or solids whose faces are all polygons such as prisms and pyramids, from other familiar three-dimensional figures such as cones, cylinders, and spheres. They describe polyhedra by numbers of edges, faces, and vertices. They also distinguish among polyhedra. For example, a triangular prism is identified by two congruent parallel triangular bases, and a square pyramid is identified by a square base. Students also decompose polyhedra, cones, and cylinders into their two-dimensional surfaces, also called *nets*.

Students' previous work with perimeter, area, and volume also helps them understand the concepts included in this Focal Point. In earlier grades, students explore the perimeter of a figure as the distance around the edge of a figure and determine that for a polygon it is the sum of the lengths of the sides. They develop and use such formulas as $P = 2(l + w)$ and $P = 8s$ to find the perimeter of certain common polygons. Students connect the concept of area to the number of square units needed to cover the interior of a figure and develop and use formulas to find the area of some polygons. For example, they use $A = lw$ to find the area of a rectangle and $A = s^2$ to find the area of a square. Students also experience developing the formulas for the area of parallelograms ($A = bh$) and triangles ($A = (1/2)bh$) using knowledge of the area formula for rectangles. In addition to experiences with two-dimensional figures, students connect the concept of volume to the number of cubes needed to fill a three-dimensional object and develop and use the formula $V = lwh$ to find the volume of rectangular prisms. Students also explore the units used to measure different attributes of figures and observe that linear units are used to measure perimeter, square units to measure area, and cubic units to measure volume.

In another grade 7 Focal Point, students see that the perimeter of a circle is called *circumference*. In their work with proportionality, they learn that π is the ratio of the circumference of a circle to its diameter, and they use π in the formula $C = \pi d$ and $C = 2\pi r$ to find the circumference of a circle if the diameter is known.

Students' previous work with expressions, equations, and formulas lays the foundation that students build on as they learn more about volume and surface area. For example, they apply their understanding of properties of addition and multiplication to write $2l + 2h$, $2(l + h)$, and $l + l + h + h$ as equivalent expressions that they can use to find the perimeter of a rectangle. They use the properties of equality to create equivalent equations, such as transforming $A = lw$ into the equivalent equation

$$\frac{A}{w} = l$$

to find length.

Focusing on Understanding and Using Formulas to Determine Surface Area and Volumes

The goal of this Focal Point is for students to understand and be able to use formulas and other computational strategies to determine surface area and volume of rectangular prisms, triangular prisms, cylinders, and composite shapes consisting of these figures. The process of understanding each formula should begin with students creating their own representations for the surface area or volume of a figure and then, with guidance from the teacher, progressing to the commonly used formula. By deriving formulas in this way, students acquire the necessary understanding to remember and apply the formulas. For students to be successful with the concepts of this Focal Point, they need a thorough understanding of the formulas for the areas of such polygons as squares, rectangles, and triangles.

In previous grades, students measure surface area and volume concretely. For example, they cover rectangular prisms with grid paper and count squares to find the surface area. They fill rectangular prisms with unit cubes to find volume. In grade 7, students make the transition from using hands-on measuring techniques to using algebraic representations (formulas) and computation to find surface area and volume. Students also gain an appreciation for the fact that using the formulas is generally more efficient and applicable to many figures for which counting methods are impractical. For example, if the dimensions of a figure are expressed as fractions or decimals, it is difficult to count squares or cubes accurately.

Reflect As You Read

Why do you think students are often confused about which measurement formula to use in a given situation, for example using $2\pi r$ instead of πr^2 to find the area of a circle or using a formula for volume to find surface area? What experiences or discussions might help them avoid this confusion?

Inherent in this Focal Point is the idea of dimensions. Just as length is a one-dimensional measure of size, area is a two-dimensional measure of the size of a region in the plane, and volume is a three-dimensional measure of a solid in three dimensions. The units used correspond to the dimensions. Teachers should help students develop an understanding of the various types of units through experiences such as the one shown in figure 3.1.

When students work with surface area and volume of three-dimensional figures, teachers should reinforce these ideas by focusing students' attention on the meanings of the answers, including the units needed. The table in figure 3.2 summarizes the relationships among measurements, dimensions, and measurement units.

Area of a circle

In this Focal Point, students learn that many of the formulas for surface area and volume of three-dimensional figures include, in some form, the formula for the area of one or more of a figure's two-dimensional faces. For this reason, it is essential that students know how to find the area of two-dimensional figures. Prior to grade 7, students work with the formulas for the areas of polygons, such as rectangles ($A = lw$), squares ($A = s^2$), and triangles ($A = (1/2) bh$). Once students understand π as the ratio

$$\frac{C}{d} \text{ or } \frac{C}{2r},$$

they can begin to understand the formula for the area of a circle. Although calculus is required to formally derive the formula for the area of a circle, the following representational progression is helpful for students to begin to gain a conceptual understanding of the formula for the area of a circle: $A = \pi r^2$.

One-Dimensional Measure: Length
To measure one-dimensional objects, start by defining what it means to have length 1.

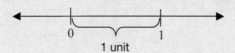

Place 0 and 1 on the number line to create a line segment of length 1 unit. This line segment can represent 1 unit of any linear measure; for example, the segment could be equal to 1 centimeter (1 cm or cm^1).

Two-Dimensional Measure: Area
In two dimensions, choose a region whose "size" is 1.

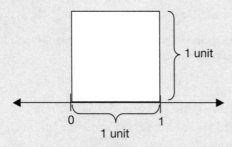

Look at a 1 × 1 square using the unit of length, and say that the measure of that region is 1 square unit. For example, if a centimeter is the unit of length, instead of inventing a brand-new name for the unit of measure of a 1 × 1 square, say that the square has a two-dimensional measure equal to 1 "square centimeter" and use cm^2 as the notation, thus emphasizing the use of the one-dimensional unit, centimeter.

Three-Dimensional Measure: Volume
In three dimensions, choose a three-dimensional solid whose "size" is 1.

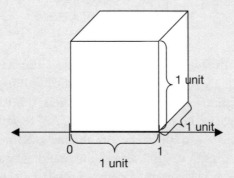

Look at a 1 × 1 × 1 cube using the unit of length, and say that the measure of that solid is 1 cubic unit. For example, if a centimeter is the unit of length, instead of inventing a brand-new name for the unit of measure of a 1 × 1 × 1 cube, say that the cube has a three-dimensional measure equal to 1 "cubic centimeter" and use cm^3 as the notation, thus emphasizing the use of the one-dimensional unit, centimeter.

Fig. 3.1. Experience that helps students develop an understanding of different units

Measures of Geometric Figures				
Attribute Being Measured	**Dimensions**	**Examples of Figures**	**Examples of Measurement Units**	**Distinguishing Characteristic of Formulas**
Length (including perimeter and circumference)	1	line segment polygon circle	inch meter	linear measures, sometimes added together
Area (including surface area)	2	polygon circle	square inch square meter	two linear measures multiplied together
Volume	3	polyhedron cylinder	cubic inch cubic meter	three linear measures multiplied together or an area measure and a linear measure multiplied together

Fig. 3.2. Comparing and contrasting one-dimensional, two-dimensional, and three-dimensional measurements

A sector of a circle, as shown in figure 3.3, is a region bounded by two radii and their intercepted arc. Sectors are shaped like "pizza slices."

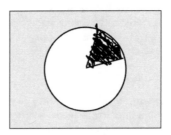

Fig. 3.3. Sector of a circle

If the circle with radius r is sliced into an even number of congruent sectors and the sectors are rearranged into a row, the resulting figure would resemble a parallelogram with the radius of the circle, r, as its "height," and half of the circumference of the circle, or πr, as its "base," as shown in figure 3.4.

If you were able to slice the circle into thinner and thinner sectors, the curved edges would appear straighter and the resulting figure would more and more resemble the parallelogram. The area of this parallelogram can be found by multiplying the base, πr, by the height, r, or $A = \pi r \cdot r$, which can also be written πr^2. Through this method of illustrating the area of a circle, students can see that, since the area of the circle is coming closer and closer to the area of the parallelogram, it makes sense that the area of the circle is: $A = \pi r^2$.

Surface areas of prisms

Students learn that the formulas for the areas of two-dimensional figures can be used to find the surface area of a three-dimensional figure. In initial dis-

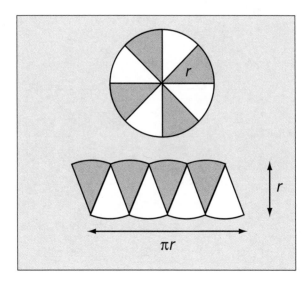

Fig. 3.4. Sectors of a circle arranged in a row to approximate a parallelogram

cussions of surface area, the rectangular prism provides a good example from which the discussion can then be expanded.

Teacher: Let's find the surface area of this 3-by-4-by-6 rectangular prism that I covered with grid paper.

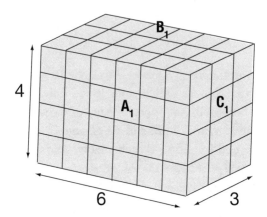

We can unfold the cover of the prism into a net so that all its faces are laid flat. Now find the surface area. Notice that surface area, although it refers to a three-dimensional object, is a two-dimensional measurement, just like the area of a square or triangle.

Tam, can you tell us how you found the surface area?

Tam: Sure. I know that the surface area is the number of square units in all the faces of the figure. So I counted the square units on the net of the figure. There are 108 squares, so the surface area is 108 square units.

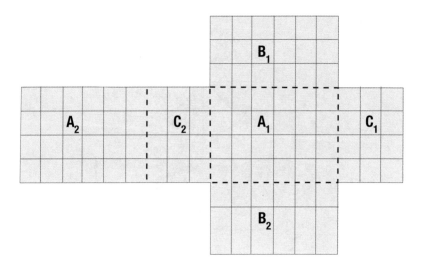

Maari: I started to count the squares, but it was taking a long time. I noticed that the faces were all rectangles, so I decided to use the formula for rectangles: $A = lw$. I used the formula to find the area of all the faces:

$$A_1 = 6 \cdot 4 = 24$$
$$A_2 = 6 \cdot 4 = 24$$
$$B_1 = 6 \cdot 3 = 18$$
$$B_2 = 6 \cdot 3 = 18$$
$$C_1 = 3 \cdot 4 = 12$$
$$C_2 = 3 \cdot 4 = 12$$

Then I added them all together: $S = 24 + 24 + 18 + 18 + 12 + 12 = 108$,

Teacher: Interesting, Maari. Did anyone do it a different way?

Shakeem: I did. I realized that opposite pairs of faces were congruent, so they had the same area: A_1 and A_2, B_1 and B_2, C_1 and C_2. So I just found the area of A_1, B_1, and C_1 and I multiplied each area by 2 and added those numbers: $24 \times 2 = 48$; $18 \times 2 = 36$; $12 \times 2 = 24$; $48 + 36 + 24 = 108$. That seemed easier to me than doing them all separately.

Teacher: We know that we can use algebraic representations to represent the strategies we use to calculate measurements of figures. Then these algebraic representations can lead us to efficient formulas. Let's look at the prism with the dimensions labeled and use it to develop an algebraic representation for the surface area of a rectangular prism.

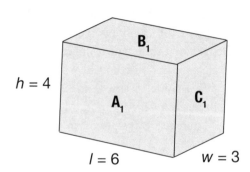

Look at Maari's method of finding the surface area. What are the length, width, and height of this prism? [$l = 6$, $w = 3$, $h = 4$.] What dimensions of the prism do you multiply to find the area of the face labeled A_1? [length and height] Why? [Because they are the dimensions of the face A_1.] Now let's remember what Shakeem observed. In a rectangular prism, the faces opposite each other, like A_1 and A_2, are the same shape and size—they are congruent—so the area of the face labeled A_2 can also be found by multiplying the prism's length times height. What dimensions of the prism do you multiply to find the areas of the faces labeled B_1 (and B_2)? [length and width] Why? [Because those are the dimensions of the faces also.] What dimensions of the prism do you multiply to find the areas of the faces labeled C_1 (and C_2)? [width and height] Why? [Because those are the dimensions of those faces.] Let's organize our results. We will use the labels on the faces to represent their areas, and S to represent the total surface area.

$$A_1 = A_2 = lh$$
$$B_1 = B_2 = lw$$
$$C_1 = C_2 = wh$$

So

$$S = A_1 + A_2 + B_1 + B_2 + C_1 + C_2 .$$

If we substitute equal values from above, then

$$S = A_1 + A_1 + B_1 + B_1 + C_1 + C_1.$$

And if we apply the distributive property, which tells us that $1x + 1x = (1+1)$ $x = 2x$, then

$$S = 2A_1 + 2B_1 + 2C_1.$$

And look, we now have an equation that represents Shakeem's method—when he found the area of A_1, B_1, and C_1 and multiplied those areas by 2 and added them together. We have used algebraic notation to show that the two strategies are equivalent.

We can take a step beyond Shakeem's method by replacing the areas with the products of the dimensions to make a formula that can be used for all rectangular prisms:

$$S = 2lh + 2lw + 2wh$$

Now we can use this formula to find the surface area of this rectangular prism:

$$S = 2 \times 24 + 2 \times 18 + 2 \times 12$$
$$S = 48 + 36 + 24$$
$$S = 108$$

The surface area of this rectangular prism is 108 square units.

Through these types of discussions, students gain practice with the understandings they need to derive a formula for the surface area of any prism, regardless of the shape of its bases: $S = 2B + Ph$. In this formula, S is the surface area, B is the area of the base, P is the perimeter of the base, and h is the height of the prism. Using the rectangular prism and its net, the formula developed in the classroom discussion, $S = 2lh + 2lw + 2wh$, and what they know about algebraic representation, students can develop this important and generalizable formula. Students learn that the basis for this formula is the understanding that a prism consists of two bases and a lateral surface area. The lateral surface area is a rectangle that "wraps around" the base of a prism. The length of the lateral surface area is the perimeter of the base, and its width is the height of the prism. Representations, such as the one shown in figure 3.5, can help students visualize this concept.

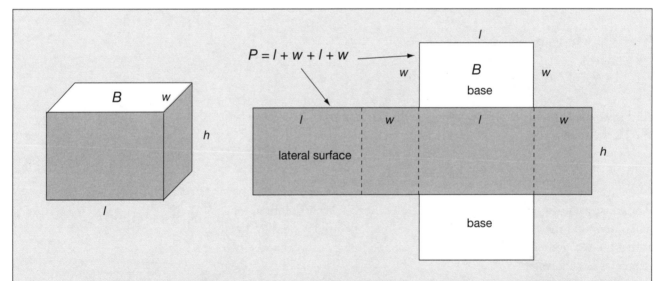

The lateral surface of a prism consists of the faces that are not identified as bases. The net shows that the lateral surface, when folded out flat, is a rectangle.

The dimensions of the rectangle that forms the lateral surface of a prism are the height of the prism and the sum of the length + width + length + width, which is also the perimeter (P) of the base. So the area of the lateral surface area is the perimeter times the height or,

$$L = Ph,$$

where L is the lateral surface area, P is the perimeter of the base, and h is the height of the prism.

Fig. 3.5. Example showing the reasoning behind the algebraic representation of the area of the lateral surface of a prism

The surface area formula, then, is the sum of the areas of the bases (which are congruent, so it is two times the area of one base) plus the area of the lateral surface (which is the perimeter of the base times the height), or $S = 2B + Ph$. Once students understand this formula conceptually, they can use algebraic representation to discover how the formula for the surface area of a rectangular prism suggests the same general formula, as shown in figure 3.6. Students will need opportunities to apply this reasoning to a variety of prisms to strengthen their understanding of the general nature of the formula.

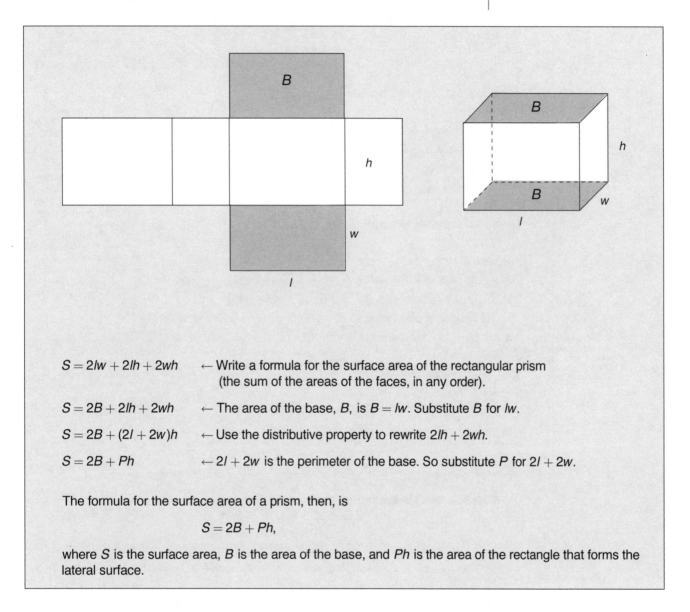

$S = 2lw + 2lh + 2wh$ ← Write a formula for the surface area of the rectangular prism (the sum of the areas of the faces, in any order).

$S = 2B + 2lh + 2wh$ ← The area of the base, B, is $B = lw$. Substitute B for lw.

$S = 2B + (2l + 2w)h$ ← Use the distributive property to rewrite $2lh + 2wh$.

$S = 2B + Ph$ ← $2l + 2w$ is the perimeter of the base. So substitute P for $2l + 2w$.

The formula for the surface area of a prism, then, is

$$S = 2B + Ph,$$

where S is the surface area, B is the area of the base, and Ph is the area of the rectangle that forms the lateral surface.

Fig. 3.6. Developing a formula for finding the surface area of a prism with base B and height h

A cube is a special case of a rectangular prism—it is a rectangular prism with six congruent square faces. Students may apply their algebraic and geometric knowledge to find the surface area of a cube in several ways, three of which are shown in figure 3.7. Discussing the similarities among these different procedures can strengthen students' understanding of the relationships between the characteristics of the three-dimensional figures and the formulas.

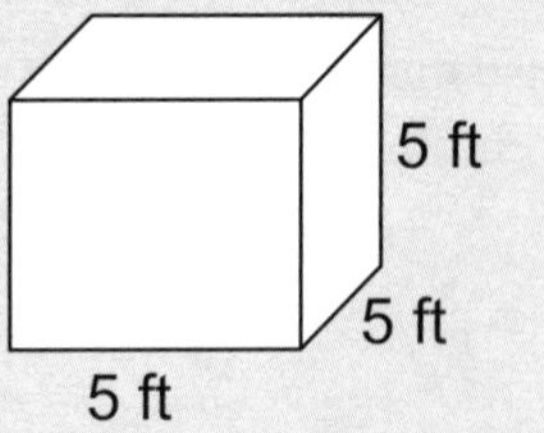

Solution Method 1:
Find the sum of the areas of all the faces.
Area of each face $= 5 \times 5 = 5^2 = 25$.
There are 6 congruent faces, so
$S = 25 + 25 + 25 + 25 + 25 + 25 = 150$
or
$S = 6 \times 25 = 150$.
The surface area is 150 square feet, or 150 ft^2.

Solution Method 2:
Use the formula $S = 2lw + 2lh + 2wh$.
$S = 2 \times 5 \times 5 + 2 \times 5 \times 5 + 2 \times 5 \times 5$
$S = 50 + 50 + 50$
$S = 150$
The surface area is 150 square feet, or 150 ft^2.

Solution Method 2:
Use the formula $S = 2B + Ph$.
B is the area of a base, so $B = 5 \times 5 = 25$ square feet.
P is the perimeter of a base, so $P = 5 + 5 + 5 + 5 = 20$ feet.
h is the height of the cube, so $h = 5$ feet.
$S = 2B + Ph$
$S = 2 \times 25 + 20 \times 5$
$S = 50 + 100$
$S = 150$
The surface area is 150 square feet, or 150 ft^2.

Fig. 3.7. Three ways to find the surface area of a cube with dimensions 5 feet by 5 feet by 5 feet

Once teachers have given students many opportunities to find the surface area of cubes in different ways, students will be ready to understand the formula of the surface area of a cube. They should then transform algebraically the formulas for surface area of rectangular prisms into the formula for surface area of cubes, as shown in figure 3.8, and see that no matter which method they use to find the surface area of a cube, they are always multiplying the square of the length of the side by 6.

Students should have similar experiences with finding the surface area of triangular prisms, as reflected in the previous classroom discussion with

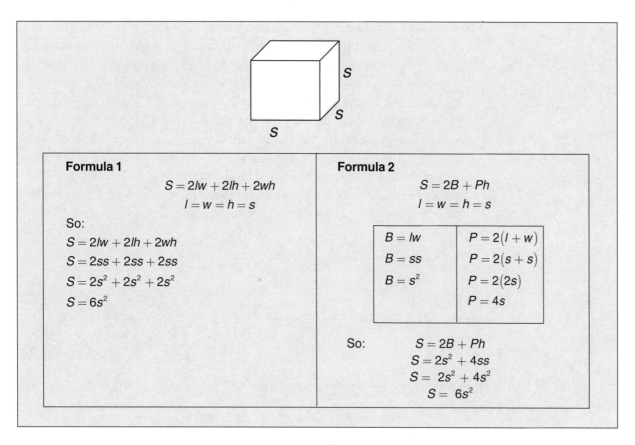

Formula 1

$$S = 2lw + 2lh + 2wh$$
$$l = w = h = s$$

So:

$$S = 2lw + 2lh + 2wh$$
$$S = 2ss + 2ss + 2ss$$
$$S = 2s^2 + 2s^2 + 2s^2$$
$$S = 6s^2$$

Formula 2

$$S = 2B + Ph$$
$$l = w = h = s$$

$B = lw$	$P = 2(l + w)$
$B = ss$	$P = 2(s + s)$
$B = s^2$	$P = 2(2s)$
	$P = 4s$

So:
$$S = 2B + Ph$$
$$S = 2s^2 + 4ss$$
$$S = 2s^2 + 4s^2$$
$$S = 6s^2$$

Fig. 3.8. Transforming the formulas for surface area of a rectangular prism into the formula for the surface area of a cube

rectangular prisms. During such discussions, teachers need to emphasize that in a triangular prism, we find two different uses of the words *base* and *height* as shown in figure 3.9. The prism itself has a measurement called its height, and the triangular faces are called the bases of the prism. Then, a triangular face that is a base of the prism also has a base (which could be any one of the sides of the triangle) and a measurement that is the height of the triangle in relation to that base of the triangle. The area of the base of a fig-

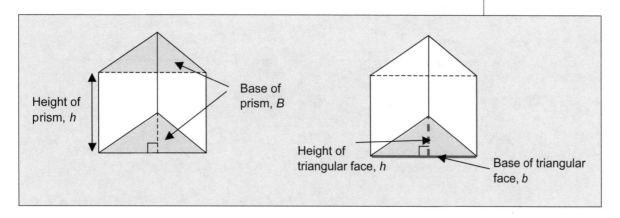

Fig. 3.9. Heights and bases of a triangular prism

ure is usually denoted by a *B*, to distinguish it from the base of the triangular face, which is denoted with a *b*. Students should have several experiences just identifying these components in various triangular prisms.

After many experiences that include using nets and grid paper and formulas to find the areas of separate faces, students can be better prepared to make connections to, and use the generalized formula for, all prisms—*S* = 2*B* + *Ph*—to find the surface area of a triangular prism. Students learn to recognize that the area of the lateral surface of the triangular prism is the perimeter of the triangular base times the height of the prism. They will gain the ability to transition from finding the surface area by adding the areas of the sides to using the general formula for surface area, as shown in figure 3.10.

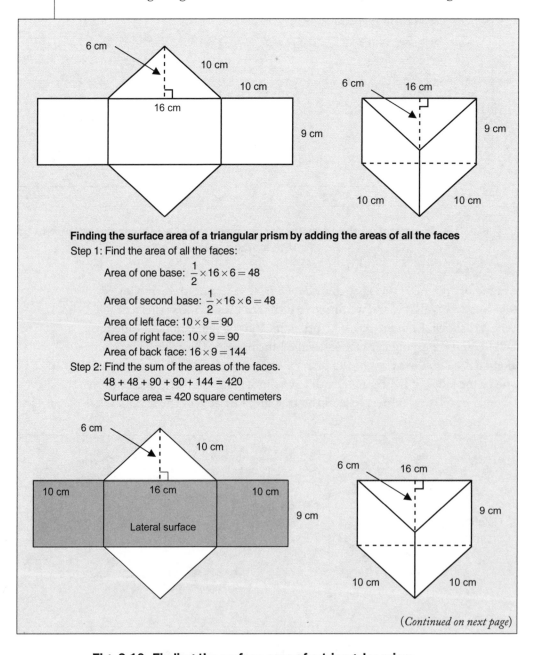

Finding the surface area of a triangular prism by adding the areas of all the faces

Step 1: Find the area of all the faces:

Area of one base: $\frac{1}{2} \times 16 \times 6 = 48$

Area of second base: $\frac{1}{2} \times 16 \times 6 = 48$

Area of left face: $10 \times 9 = 90$

Area of right face: $10 \times 9 = 90$

Area of back face: $16 \times 9 = 144$

Step 2: Find the sum of the areas of the faces.

$48 + 48 + 90 + 90 + 144 = 420$

Surface area = 420 square centimeters

(Continued on next page)

Fig. 3.10. Finding the surface area of a triangular prism

Finding the surface area of a triangular prism by using a general surface area formula $S = 2B + Ph$

Step 1: Find the area of the prism's base, $B = \dfrac{1}{2}(16)(6) = 48$; 48 square centimeters.

Step 2: Find the perimeter of the base of the prism, $P = 10 + 16 + 10 = 36$; 36 centemeters.

Step 3: Substitute the values for the formula:

$S = 2B + Ph$

$S = 2(48) + 36(9)$

$S = 96 + 324$

$S = 420$

Surface area = 420 square centimeters.

Fig. 3.10. Finding the surface area of a triangular prism—*Continued*

Once students understand the formula $S = 2B + Ph$ and can apply it to a variety of prisms, they are ready to begin to explore the surface area of cylinders. Although a cylinder is not a polyhedron, it shares some characteristics with a prism that apply to finding surface area. As students examine the nets of various prisms and cylinders, they see that cylinders, like prisms, are made up of three basic components—two congruent bases and a lateral surface that "wraps around" the bases. As with prisms, if they find the total area of these components of a cylinder, they will have found the surface area of the cylinder. As students continue to investigate the commonalities in the nets, they should recognize that when we represent the prism or cylinder by using a net for the object, we see that the total lateral surface is a rectangle, as shown in figure 3.11.

Thus, the general formula for surface area will also be able to be applied to a cylinder, since the formula is based on geometric characteristics that exist in both prisms and cylinders. Once students see these common characteristics, they can see that they can find the surface area of a cylinder using the same general formula they developed to find the surface area of prisms, that is, finding the sum of the areas of the two bases (two times the area of one base) and the area of the rectangle that creates the lateral surface. With regard to a cylinder, the area of the base (B) is the area of the circular base, and the dimensions of the rectangle that forms the lateral surface are the perimeter (or circumference) of the circular base and the height of the cylinder, as shown in figure 3.12. Students can then apply the formula presented in figure 3.12 in a meaningful way, as shown in the example in figure 3.13.

As students' comfort level with applying the surface area formulas increases, teachers should offer students the opportunity to apply these formulas to problems involving rational number dimensions. In problems involving measurements expressed with fractions, students may want to use 22/7 or 3.14 as an approximate value for π.

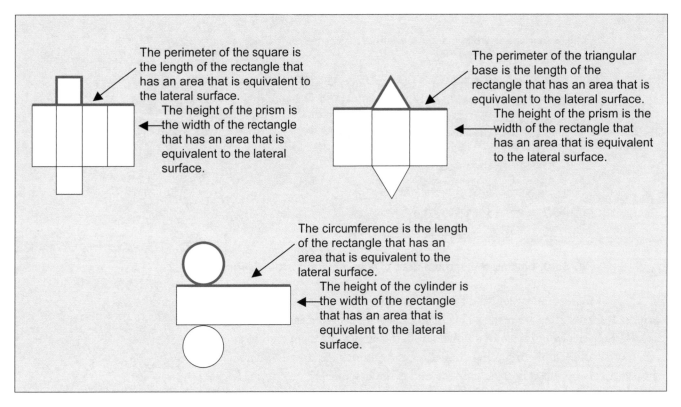

The perimeter of the square is the length of the rectangle that has an area that is equivalent to the lateral surface.
The height of the prism is the width of the rectangle that has an area that is equivalent to the lateral surface.

The perimeter of the triangular base is the length of the rectangle that has an area that is equivalent to the lateral surface.
The height of the prism is the width of the rectangle that has an area that is equivalent to the lateral surface.

The circumference is the length of the rectangle that has an area that is equivalent to the lateral surface.
The height of the cylinder is the width of the rectangle that has an area that is equivalent to the lateral surface.

Fig. 3.11. Examples showing the components of prisms and cylinders—two bases and a lateral surface

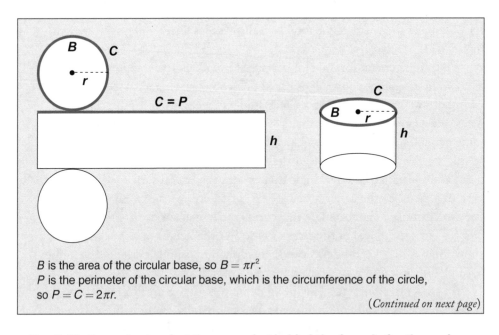

B is the area of the circular base, so $B = \pi r^2$.
P is the perimeter of the circular base, which is the circumference of the circle, so $P = C = 2\pi r$.

(*Continued on next page*)

Fig. 3.12. Example showing the reasoning behind the formula for the surface area of a cylinder

So:

$S = 2B + Ph$ ← The generalized surface area formula.
The perimeter of the base is the circumference, so replace P with C.

$S = 2B + Ch$ ← Replace B with the formula for the area of a circle, πr^2.
Replace C with the formula for the circumference of a circle, $2\pi r$.

$S = 2\pi r^2 + 2\pi rh$

Fig. 3.12. Example showing the reasoning behind the formula for the surface area of a cylinder—*Continued*

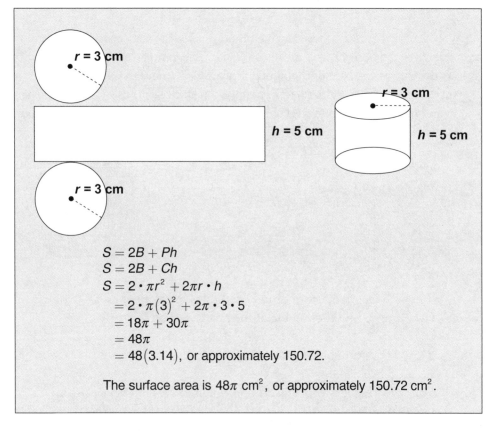

$S = 2B + Ph$
$S = 2B + Ch$
$S = 2 \cdot \pi r^2 + 2\pi r \cdot h$
$\quad = 2 \cdot \pi (3)^2 + 2\pi \cdot 3 \cdot 5$
$\quad = 18\pi + 30\pi$
$\quad = 48\pi$
$\quad = 48(3.14)$, or approximately 150.72.

The surface area is 48π cm^2, or approximately 150.72 cm^2.

Fig. 3.13. Applying the formula for the surface area of a cylinder

Volume of prisms and cylinders

As part of a focused grade 7 curriculum, students learn to meaningfully apply volume formulas to a variety of solid figures. Students can use their understanding of the characteristics of three-dimensional objects, their understanding of the meaning of volume, and their ability to apply the volume of a rectangular prism to derive the generalized volume formula. They can then use this formula to find the volume of other solids. Teachers should structure classroom activities so that students can synthesize these understandings, as shown in the following classroom discussion.

Teacher: Look at this rectangular prism. If we find the volume of this figure, what attribute are we describing?

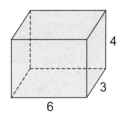

John: We have found the number of cubic units that it takes to fill the figure.

Teacher: Correct. If we imagine filling the figure with cubes, we might first cover the bottom, or base, of the figure. This one "layer" of cubes covers the area of the base of the figure; it takes 6 × 3 cubes to make the layer that covers the rectangular base. Then we can stack layers as indicated by the height of the prism. In this rectangular prism the height is 4, so there are four layers.

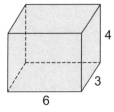 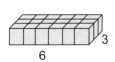 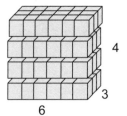

A prism with length 6, width 3, and height 4 is made up of four 6-by-3 layers. How can we find the volume of the prism in cubic units?

Theresa: You can multiply the length times the width times the height, or 6 × 3 × 4 = 84 cubic units.

Teacher: What is the formula for the volume of a rectangular prism?

George: I know it; it is $V = lwh$.

Teacher: So if we use the formula, we will find the volume in the same way as Theresa did, by multiplying the length times the width times the height. We can think about the volume in a different way; 6 times 3 is the area of the base, 4 is the height. So you can think of volume as the area of the base (the number of cubes in one layer) times the height (the number of layers). Just as in the surface area formulas, we can represent the area of the base as B. So the formula can be written $V = Bh$, where B is the area of the base of the prism and h is the height of the prism.

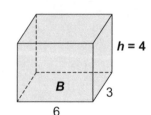

At this point, students are ready to move to understanding the formula for the volume of any prism or cylinder. Again, this is an example of when it is pedagogically appropriate for students to focus on the characteristics that are common to prisms and cylinders rather than on their differences. Through sketches and models, students can begin to visualize for any prism or cylinder a layer covering the area of the base that is one unit thick. Thus, the volume of this layer would be the area of the base $(B) \times 1 = B$. The volume of the prism or cylinder could then be visualized as a stack of these layers, with the height of the prism indicating the number of those layers in the figure, as illustrated in figure 3.14. Of course, it is possible that a fraction of a layer might be involved. Thus, the generalized volume formula, $V = Bh$, can be used to find the volume of any prism or cylinder.

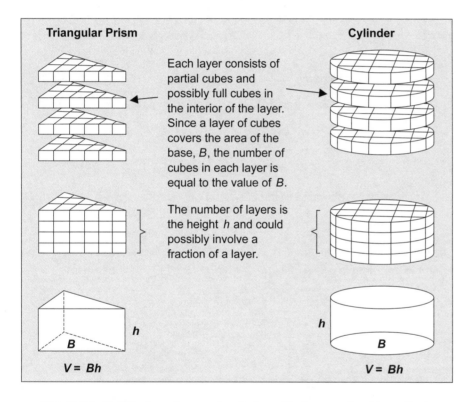

Fig. 3.14. Building a prism and cylinder with layers of cubic units to demonstrate the generalized volume formula $V = Bh$

Teachers should emphasize that although only a triangular prism is shown in figure 3.14, the same reasoning applies to all prisms. Students can then use this general formula, $V = Bh$, to meaningfully generate the formulas for volumes of the cylinder and other prisms, as shown in figure 3.15.

Rectangular Prism:

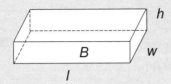

$V = Bh$
$V = lwh$ ← The base is a rectangle, so
the area of the base is $B = lw$.

Cube:

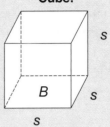

$V = Bh$
$V = lwh$
$V = sss$ ← The base is a square, so
the area of the base is $B = s \cdot s = s^2$.

Triangular Prism:

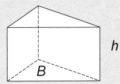

Base of Prism

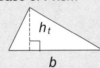

$V = Bh$
$V = \left(\dfrac{1}{2}bh_t\right)h$ ← The base is a triangle, so the area of the base is

$$B = \dfrac{1}{2}bh_t,$$

where b is the edge that is being used as a base of the triangular face, h_t
is the height of the triangle with relation to b, and h is the height of the prism.

Cylinder:

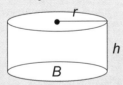

$V = Bh$
$V = \pi r^2 h$ ← The base of the cylinder is a circle, so
the area of the base is $B = \pi r^2$.

Fig. 3.15. Applying the generalized volume formula to various prisms and cylinders

Strengthening Understanding of Volume and Surface Area through Problem Solving

Students can strengthen their understanding of volume and surface area and appreciate the relevance of these concepts by solving context-based problems. Problem-solving opportunities should be structured to help students focus on important aspects of using surface area and volume in practical situations. These opportunities should include demonstrating the difference between measurements of surface area and volume, developing an understanding of the formulas for the volume of pyramids and cones, and solving problems involving composite, or compound, figures.

Problems like the one in figure 3.16 can help students distinguish between surface area and volume, that is, that surface area is a measure of the number of square units required to cover an object and that volume is a measure of the number of cubic units required to fill an object. These types of problems also give students the opportunity to meaningfully apply the formulas in everyday situations.

Problem:

The manager of a packaging department needs to design a box that will require no more than 450 square inches of cardboard (neglecting overlap and waste) and hold at least 550 cubic inches of material. She designs the box in the shape of a rectangular prism as shown, with length of 12 inches, width 6 inches, and height 8 inches. Does the box satisfy the requirements?

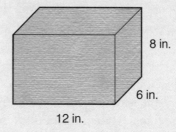

8 in.

6 in.

12 in.

Solution:

The measure of the amount of cardboard is the surface area; the measure of how much material the box will hold is the volume.

Find the surface area.	Find the volume.
The surface area S is the number of square units needed to cover the box.	The volume V is the number of cubic units needed to fill the box.

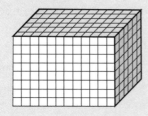

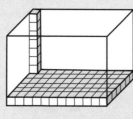

(*Continued on next page*)

Fig 3.16. Problem that helps students distinguish between surface area and volume

$S = 2lw + 2lh + 2wh$ $\quad = 2 \cdot 12 \cdot 6 + 2 \cdot 12 \cdot 8 + 2 \cdot 6 \cdot 8$ $\quad = 144 + 192 + 96$ $\quad = 432$ The surface area is 432 square inches.	$V = lwh$ $\quad = 12 \cdot 6 \cdot 8$ $\quad = 576$ The volume is 576 cubic inches.
The surface area is less than 450 square inches, and the volume is more than 550 cubic inches, so the box satisfies the requirements.	

Fig 3.16. Problem that helps students distinguish between surface area and volume—*Continued*

Although students will learn how to derive the formula for the volume of cones and pyramids in later grades, problem-solving opportunities in grade 7 will help students begin to build an intuitive understanding of the relationship between the volume of a prism and its corresponding pyramid and the volume of a cone and its corresponding cylinder. Specifically, students can begin to develop the concept that the volume of a pyramid is one-third the volume of a prism with the same base area and height, and the volume of a cone is one-third the volume of a cylinder with the same base area and height. Problems such as the one in figure 3.17 help students gain this understanding.

Problem-solving experiences involving compound, or complex, solids give students the opportunity to explore how composition and decomposition of figures affect the surface area and volume. For example, because the shapes that compose a composite solid sometimes have one or more shared surfaces that "disappear" into the interior of the composite figure, the surface area of the composite figure is not always the sum of the surface areas of the shapes that compose it. Problems like the ones shown in figure 3.18 can help students understand that often the surface area of a composite figure is less than the sum of the surface areas of the individual figures, but the volume of the composite figure is often the same as the volumes of the individual figures.

In problem 1, when students find the surface area, they need to keep in mind that the surface of the triangular prism and the surface of the rectangular prism that are shared are not included, because they are no longer part of the surface area. In this situation, students will probably find the sum of the areas of the separate faces that are still part of the surface area of the new figure rather than use surface area formulas and subtract the "missing" faces. When finding the volume, however, the entire volumes of both prisms are included in the volume of the new figure, so students can use volume formulas and add the volumes of the two prisms.

In problem 2, students need to find the volume and surface area of the pipe. The pipe is like two cylinders, one "removed" from the other. Therefore, to find the volume of the pipe, students need to find the difference between the volumes of the two cylinders, the volume that is left over when the smaller cylinder is removed from the larger cylinder. However, when the smaller

Problem 1:

How many pyramids fit inside a prism with the same base area and height? If the volume of a prism with base area B and height h is $V = Bh$, what equation can you use to represent volume V of a pyramid with base area B and height h?

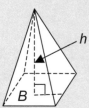 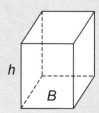 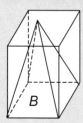

pyramid and rectangular prism with identical bases and heights

Solution:

Use a hollow plastic pyramid and rectangular prism with identical bases and heights to compare their volumes. Fill the pyramid with, for example, uncooked rice. Pour the rice into the prism. Repeat the action as many times as necessary to determine how the volume of the pyramid compares to the volume of the prism.

It takes three pours to use the pyramid to fill the corresponding prism, so the volume of the pyramid appears to be 1/3 the volume of the corresponding prism. It seems reasonable that the volume of the pyramid is

$$V = \frac{1}{3}Bh.$$

Problem 2:

How many cones fit into a cylinder with the same base and height? If the volume of a cylinder with base area B and height h is $V = Bh$, what equation can you use to represent volume V of a cone with base area B and height h?

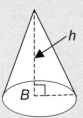 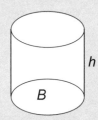 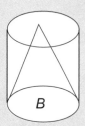

cone and cylinder with identical bases and heights

Solution:

Three pours are needed to use the cone to fill the corresponding cylinder, so the volume of the cone appears to be 1/3 the volume of the corresponding cylinder. So it seems reasonable that the volume of the cone is

$$V = \frac{1}{3}Bh.$$

Fig 3.17. Experiences that support the formulas for the volume of a pyramid and a cone

Problem 1:

You are designing a small building to serve as a workshop. To stay within a budget for building materials, you want the exterior surface area to be less than or equal to 800 square feet. To know what size air conditioner to buy, you need to know the volume inside the workshop. Your design consists of a triangular prism on top of a rectangular prism, as shown. Does the design satisfy the exterior surface requirement? What is the interior volume of the shed?

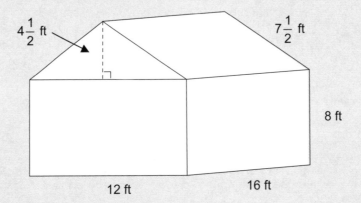

Problem 2:

The concrete pipe shown below has the shape of a cylindrical shell with an outside diameter of 1.0 meter and an inside diameter of 0.8 meter. Concrete weighs about 5300 pounds per cubic meter. What is the weight of the pipe to the nearest pound? What is the total surface area of the pipe to the nearest hundredth of a square meter?

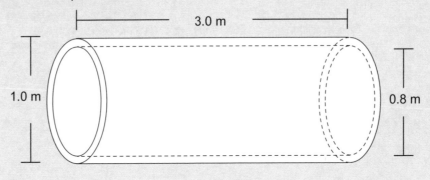

Fig 3.18. Problems involving composite figures

cylinder is removed from the larger cylinder, the surface area is affected in complex ways. To find the surface area of the pipe, students cannot just subtract the surface areas of the cylinders. In initial experiences with this type of problem, students should first be able to explain that if a "core" cylinder is removed from the inside of a larger cylinder, it causes a decrease of surface area in what used to be the bases of the larger cylinder (the circular bases become rings), but it causes an *increase* in lateral surface area because it creates a new exposed surface on the inside that is the size of the lateral surface area of the smaller cylinder that was removed. So to find the surface area of the pipe, students need to realize that the pipe has four surfaces—two "ring-shaped" ends of the pipe, the lateral surface of the outside cylinder, and the lateral surface of the inside cylinder. Students need to find the sum of the areas of these surfaces. To find the area of the ends of the pipe, students should find the difference between the areas of the circles that form the ring. To find the areas of the inside and outside of the pipe, students should find the areas of the lateral surfaces of the inside and outside cylinders, respectively. The sum of these four parts is the total surface area of the pipe.

> ### Reflect As You Read
>
> **In many contextual problems, the geometric model is already provided, for example, the description of the workshop building as a triangular prism on top of a rectangular prism. However, in these types of problems in the real world, the geometric models are not directly described and must be created by the person solving the problem. How can we help students better apply their understandings of geometric figures to model real-world situations?**

Strengthening Understanding through Connections

Through making connections among concepts, students deepen their understanding of those concepts. One connection that teachers can help students understand is the connection between measures of geometric figures and proportionality. Specifically, students should understand how perimeter, area, surface area, and volume are connected to the concepts of similarity and scale factor. They should also understand how proportionality is used to find the area of a sector of a circle.

If the dimensions of two similar figures are all in the same unit, the ratio of any pair of corresponding dimensions in the two similar figures is the scale factor for the similar figures. The example given in figure 3.19 shows two similar rectangles with a scale factor of 3/2. In other words, a linear dimension in rectangle B times 3/2 gives the corresponding linear dimension in rectangle A.

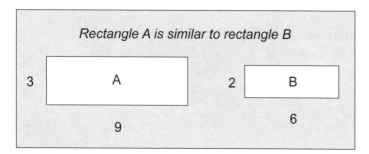

Fig. 3.19. Similar rectangles with a scale factor of 3/2

The measurements in these similar figures have a specific relationship. For example, the perimeter of rectangle *A* is 24 units and the perimeter of rectangle *B* is 16 units. The ratio of the perimeter of *A* to the perimeter of *B*, or

$$\frac{\text{perimeter of A}}{\text{perimeter of B}},$$

is

$$\frac{24}{16} = \frac{3}{2}.$$

So the ratio of perimeters is equal to the scale factor. The area of A is 27 square units, and the area of B is 12 square units. The ratio of the area of A to the area of B, or

$$\frac{\text{area of A}}{\text{area of B}},$$

is

$$\frac{27}{12} = \frac{9}{4}.$$

So the ratio of areas is equal to the square of the scale factor:

$$\frac{9}{4} = \left(\frac{3}{2}\right)^2.$$

This is a reasonable result, as the calculation of area involves the multiplication of two linear dimensions, each involving the scale factor of 3/2:

$$A = \left(\frac{3}{2}\right)l \times \left(\frac{3}{2}\right)w = \left(\frac{3}{2}\right)\left(\frac{3}{2}\right)lw = \left(\frac{3}{2}\right)^2 lw = \left(\frac{9}{4}\right)lw,$$

where *l* and *w* are the length and width of the original rectangle. As students have the opportunities to calculate and compare the areas of two-dimensional figures, including rectangles, triangles, and circles, they will begin to realize that these relationships are true for all similar figures.

Students can deepen their understanding of the connection between measurements and proportionality by exploring three-dimensional figures, as well, as shown in figure 3.20.

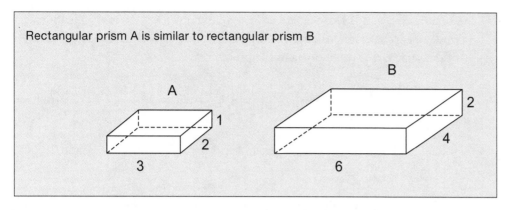

Rectangular prism A is similar to rectangular prism B

Fig. 3.20. Similar rectangular prisms with a scale factor of 1/2

The measurements of three-dimensional figures also have a specific relationship. For example, the scale factor of the prisms in figure 3.20 is 1/2. The surface area of A is 22 square units. The surface area of B is 88 square units. So the ratio of the surface area of A to the surface area of B, or

$$\frac{\text{surface area of A}}{\text{surface area of B}},$$

is

$$\frac{22}{88} = \frac{1}{4}.$$

The ratio of the surface areas in a given order is the same as the ratio of the areas of two-dimensional figures in the same order; it is equal to the square of the scale factor:

$$\frac{1}{4} = \left(\frac{1}{2}\right)^2.$$

The volume of A is 6 cubic units. The volume of B is 48 cubic units. The ratio of the volume of A to the volume of B, or

$$\frac{\text{volume of A}}{\text{volume of B}},$$

is

$$\frac{6}{48} = \frac{1}{8}.$$

The ratio of volumes is equal to the cube of the scale factor:

$$\frac{1}{8} = \left(\frac{1}{2}\right)^3.$$

Again, this result is reasonable because volume involves the multiplication of three linear measures, or an area and a linear measure, which involves the use of the scale factor three times in the product:

$$V = \left(\frac{1}{2}\right) l \times \left(\frac{1}{2}\right) w \times \left(\frac{1}{2}\right) h = \left(\frac{1}{2}\right)\left(\frac{1}{2}\right)\left(\frac{1}{2}\right) lwh = \left(\frac{1}{2}\right)^3 lwh = \left(\frac{1}{8}\right) lwh,$$

where l and w and h are the length and width and height of the original prism.

As students have the opportunities to calculate and compare the surface areas and volumes of similar prisms, including triangular prisms, and similar cylinders, they will begin to realize that these relationships are true for all similar three-dimensional figures. Figure 3.21 summarizes the general properties regarding scale factors, perimeter, area, surface area, and volume in similar figures.

- If the scale factor for two similar polygons is k, then the ratio of their perimeters is k (or k^1).

- If the scale factor for two similar polygons is k, then the ratio of their areas is k^2.

- If the scale factor for two similar prisms or cylinders is k, then the ratio of their surface areas is k^2.

- If the scale factor for two similar prisms or cylinders is k, then the ratio of their volumes is k^3.

Fig. 3.21. Properties showing the relationships among measurements of similar figures

Students can also connect measurement to proportionality in their exploration of finding the area of a sector of a circle. In grade 7, students learn to understand how proportionality is used in applying the formula for the area of a sector of a circle, as shown in figure 3.22.

Through connecting proportionality to measurement and completing problems such as the one shown in figure 3.22, students learn to generalize that

$$\frac{\text{area of sector}}{\pi r^2} = \frac{t}{360},$$

$$\text{area of sector} = \frac{t}{360} \pi r^2.$$

Find the area of the circle.

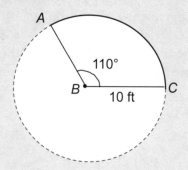

Solution:

The ratio of the sector area to the entire circle is equal to the ratio of the central angle measure to 360°.

$$\frac{\text{area of sector}}{\text{area of circle}} = \frac{110°}{360°}$$

$$\frac{\text{area of sector}}{\pi r^2} = \frac{110}{360}$$

$$\frac{\text{area of sector}}{\pi (10)^2} = \frac{110}{360}$$

$$\text{area of sector} = \frac{110}{360} \pi (10)^2$$

$$\text{area of sector} = \frac{110}{360} 100\pi$$

$$\text{area of sector} \approx \frac{110}{360} 100 (3.14)$$

$$\text{area of sector} \approx 95.94$$

The area of the sector is approximately 96 square feet.

Fig. 3.22. Example showing the connection between the area of the sector of a circle and proportionality

Or the area A of a sector of a circle with radius r is

$$\text{area of sector} = \frac{t}{360} \pi r^2,$$

where t represents the measure of the central angle of the sector in degrees.

Connections in later grades

In later grades students will use properties of two-dimensional and three-dimensional similar figures to solve increasingly more difficult problems. They will need to think not only about measures of length but also about angle measures. They will use the fact that corresponding angles in similar figures must be congruent as a method of determining whether figures are similar.

As students find surface area or volume of solid figures, they sometimes need to identify hidden or partially hidden right triangles and apply the Pythagorean theorem. For example, they might apply the Pythagorean theorem to the partially hidden right triangle, $\triangle ABC$, related to the pyramid in figure 3.23 to determine either the height (AB) or slant height (AC) of the pyramid and then use that result to find the surface area or volume.

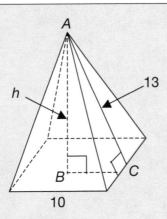

The partially hidden right triangle, $\triangle ABC$, has a hypotenuse of length 13. The bottom leg (in the base of the pyramid) has length 5, because its length is half of 10. The height, AB, of the pyramid is found by applying the Pythagorean theorem as follows.

$$h^2 + 5^2 = 13^2$$
$$h^2 + 25 = 169$$
$$h^2 = 144$$
$$h = 12$$

The volume V is found as follows:

$$V = \frac{1}{3}Bh$$
$$V = \frac{1}{3}10^2 \times 12$$
$$V = \frac{1}{3} \times 1200$$
$$V = 400$$

The volume is 400 cubic units.

Fig. 3.23. Using the dimensions of a hidden triangle and the Pythagorean theorem to find the volume of a pyramid

Developing Depth of Understanding

What activities do you do or plan to do in your classroom that can guide students to understand that the formulas for surface area and volume of three-dimensional figures compute the measurements students have previously measured directly? How can you help students understand that using formulas to find surface area and volume of three-dimensional figures is often more efficient than using other methods of determining those measurements?

4 Focusing on Understanding the Rational Number System

In grade 7 students learn how to compute with rational numbers, including negative fractions and decimals. They develop an understanding of the rational numbers as a system and how the set of whole numbers is related to the set of rational numbers. They become aware of properties that apply to the system of rational numbers but not to the system of whole numbers. The goal of this Focal Point is for students to apply their understandings of the operations and properties of the rational number system to develop the fluency needed to work with linear equations and solve problems that involve rational numbers.

Instructional Progression for Understanding the Rational Number System

The focus on rational numbers in grade 7 is supported by a progression of related mathematical ideas before and after grade 7, as shown in table 4.1. To give perspective to the grade 7 work, we first discuss some of the important ideas that students focused on before grade 7 that prepare them for learning about rational numbers in grade 7. At the end of the detailed discussion of this grade 7 Focal Point, we present examples of how students will use rational number understandings and skills in later grades. For more detailed discussions of the "before" and "after" parts of the instructional progression, please see the appropriate grade level books, *Focus in Grade 3*, *Focus in Grade 4*, *Focus in Grade 5*, *Focus in Grade 6*, and *Focus in Grade 8*.

Table 4.1 represents an instructional progression for the conceptual understanding of rational numbers before grade 7, during grade 7, and after grade 7.

Early Foundations for Understanding Rational Numbers

Prior to grade 7, students are expected to have learned skills and concepts that prepare them for understanding how to compute with rational numbers and how to solve equations involving rational numbers. In previous grades, students perform addition, subtraction, multiplication, and division with nonnegative rational numbers, that is, whole numbers, positive fractions, and positive decimals. They model everyday situations with negative integers. They also work with expressions, equations, and formulas. Students build on these prior understandings to learn how to operate with all rational numbers and to solve equations involving rational numbers.

Table 4.1

Grade 7: Focusing on Understanding the Rational Number System—Instructional Progression for Rational Numbers

Before Grade 7	Grade 7	After Grade 7
Students develop an understanding of fractions and fraction equivalence. Students develop an understanding of decimals, including the connection between fractions and decimals. Students develop efficient, accurate, and generalizable methods for operating with positive rational numbers. Students use operations with positive rational numbers to solve problems. Students begin to develop the ability to generalize numerical relationships and express mathematical ideas concisely using expressions and equations (e.g., three more as $x + 3$, doubling as $2n$, commutativity as $a + b = b + a$). Students solve simple one-step equations by using number sense, properties of operations, and the idea of maintaining equality on both sides of an equation and understand that the solutions of an equation are the values of the variables that make the equation true. Students develop the skills to use expressions, equations, and formulas to solve problems (e.g., apply the understanding of equivalent expressions to decide between the use of $5x$ or $2x + 3x$ in the solution to a problem). Students explore contexts that they can describe with negative numbers, e.g., situations of owing money or measuring elevations above and below sea level.	Students develop a thorough understanding of negative numbers (including negative decimals and decimal fractions). Students use models of negative numbers to represent and justify rules for adding, subtracting, multiplying, and dividing with negative numbers. Students develop efficient, accurate, and generalizable methods for operating with negative numbers. Students develop an understanding of the relationships between sets of numbers (whole numbers, integers, rationals), properties of these sets of numbers, and operations with each set, including closure; commutative, associative, and distributive laws; additive identity; multiplicative identity; additive inverses; and multiplicative inverses. Students recognize fractions, percents, and certain decimals as ways of representing rational numbers and convert flexibly between fractions, decimals, and percents. Students are able to explain which fractions correspond to terminating decimals. Students use linear equations in one variable and rational numbers to solve word problems.	Students use exponents and scientific notation to describe very large and very small numbers.* Students use square roots when they apply the Pythagorean theorem.* Students develop an understanding of the concept of function and how linear equations can be studied as functions. Students translate among algebraic, geometric (graphical), numerical (tabular), and verbal representations of linear functions. Students relate systems of equations to pairs of lines that intersect, are parallel, or are the same line in the plane and understand that the solution to a system of equations is a solution to both equations. Students analyze and solve problems using linear equations and systems of linear equations.

*Appears in the Grade 8 Connections to the Focal Points (NCTM 2006).

Nonnegative rational numbers and integers

All whole numbers, positive fractions, terminating decimals, and repeating decimals are rational numbers, so every skill and concept involving these numbers with which students have previously worked has helped prepare them to understand rational numbers. Students are expected to have developed an understanding of fractions and fraction equivalence in previous grades. They learn to add and subtract fractions with unlike denominators and work with ratios and equivalent ratios. They are expected to develop an understanding of decimals as representations of fractions whose denominators are powers of ten and to learn to convert between fractions and decimals. They use the relationship between decimals and fractions to help understand and explain procedures for multiplying and dividing decimals. Students also begin to develop an understanding of negative integers. In grade 5 students explore contexts that they can describe with negative integers; for example, they model "owing 5 dollars" as –5 and "25 feet below sea level" as –25.

In previous grades students also are expected to have developed efficient, accurate, and generalizable methods for operating with positive rational numbers and use operations with positive rational numbers to solve problems. In particular, they add, subtract, multiply, and divide whole numbers and positive fractions and decimals. When dividing whole numbers, they express results as whole numbers, fractions, mixed numbers, or decimals.

Expressions, equations, and formulas

Prior to grade 7, students generalize numerical relationships and express mathematical ideas concisely using expressions and equations. For example, they represent the commutative property as $a + b = b + a$ and "two times a number plus 5" as $2x + 5$. Students also evaluate algebraic expressions by substituting numbers for variables and simplifying the resulting numerical expressions; for example, if $n = 4$, then $n + 5 = 4 + 5 = 9$. They are expected to develop the skills to use expressions, equations, and formulas to solve problems and learn to write equivalent expressions and equations, such as writing $5x$ as $2x + 3x$ and $x - 4 = y$ as $x = y + 4$. Students also solve simple one-step equations by using different strategies, including number sense, properties of operations, and properties of equality. Students see that a solution of an equation is a value of a variable that makes the equation true. For example, they can verify that 15 is the solution of $n - 5 = 10$ because $15 - 5 = 10$ is true.

Focusing on Understanding the Rational Number System

A number system is a set of numbers together with the operations and properties that apply to that set. Entering grade 7, students are already familiar with the whole-number system, that is, the numbers {0, 1, 2, 3...} and the operations of addition, subtraction, multiplication, and division and their properties. In grade 7 students learn to think about certain fractions and decimals and the operations as elements of the rational number system. In grade 7 students discover that the rational number system shares some characteristics with the whole-number system, but there are also some differences. To present the rational numbers as a system, teachers can cluster concepts into three categories—the numbers, the definitions and properties of the operations, and computational procedures. Through exploration of the similarities and differences among whole numbers, integers, and rational numbers with regard to these three areas, students can gain a more complete understanding of both whole numbers and rational numbers as systems.

Rational numbers

A rational number is a number that can be written in the form

$$\frac{a}{b},$$

where a and b are integers and $b \neq 0$. Students should note that integers fit this definition, so integers are also rational numbers. Every rational number can be expressed as either a terminating or repeating decimal. Examples of rational numbers are 8/2 = 4, 3/–1 = –3, 3/8 = 0.375, and –18/11 = –1.63$\overline{63}$. Students are familiar with 0 and the positive rational numbers from their work with fractions and decimals in grades 5 and 6. By including negative rational numbers in grade 7, they learn to work with the entire set of rational numbers. Students also learn to compare and order rational numbers and how to identify additive inverses, multiplicative inverses, and absolute values. One model that helps students acquire these understandings is the number-line model. Students can use the number-line model to get a sense of the value of a number in relation to other numbers, as shown in figure 4.1.

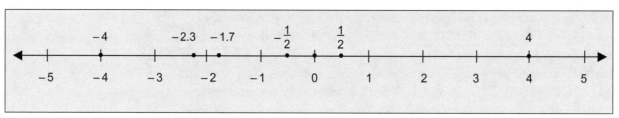

Fig. 4.1. Using the number line to develop an understanding of rational numbers

The *absolute value* of a number is the distance between the number and zero. The absolute value symbol is | |; so, for example, the absolute value of –4 is indicated by | –4 |. Because an absolute value is a distance, it is never negative. The absolute values of several numbers in figure 4.1 are

$$\left|-4\right|=4, \left|4\right|=4, \left|-\frac{1}{2}\right|=\frac{1}{2}, \left|2.3\right|=2.3, \text{ and } \left|0\right|=0.$$

Two nonzero rational numbers are *opposites* if they have the same absolute value but are on opposite sides of zero on a number line. Referring to figure 4.1, the numbers –4 and 4 are opposites. The numbers

$$-\frac{1}{2}$$

and

$$\frac{1}{2}$$

are also opposites. Zero is the only number that has an absolute value of 0, so the opposite of 0 is 0. Every rational number has an opposite. Students use the concept of opposites to help them understand why the rules for computing with negative numbers make sense. Having a solid understanding of opposites, that is, additive inverses, is important to students' understanding of rational numbers.

In grade 7 students learn about the relationship among the sets of rational numbers, integers, and whole numbers. The diagram shown in figure 4.2 can help students visualize this relationship. From the Venn diagram, students can see that the set of integers is a subset of the set of rational numbers. In other words, every integer is a rational number. Also, the set of whole numbers is a subset of the set of integers, and so also a subset of the set of rational numbers. That is, every whole number is an integer and a rational number.

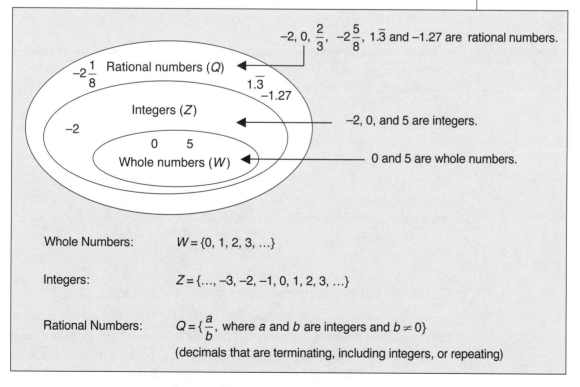

Whole Numbers: $W = \{0, 1, 2, 3, \ldots\}$

Integers: $Z = \{\ldots, -3, -2, -1, 0, 1, 2, 3, \ldots\}$

Rational Numbers: $Q = \{\frac{a}{b}$, where a and b are integers and $b \neq 0\}$
(decimals that are terminating, including integers, or repeating)

Fig. 4.2. Venn diagram showing the relationship among the sets of whole numbers, integers, and rational numbers

As students have opportunities to model rational numbers—for example, locating rational numbers on the number line—they can build the understanding needed to compare and order these numbers. From previous work with number lines, students should know that the farther to the left a number is located on the number line, the less its value. So they can determine that negative numbers are less than positive numbers and that the farther away a negative number is from 0, the less it is; for example, –2 is less than –1.5. Students use the comparison symbols >, <, ≥, and ≤ to compare rational numbers. Figure 4.3 shows the types of comparisons that students should be able to make with this reasoning.

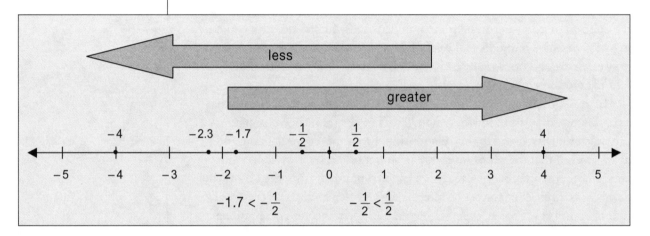

Fig. 4.3. Rational number comparison

Students also learn how to compare absolute values of rational numbers. For example, students can determine that $|-4| > |-2.2|$ because –4 is farther from 0 than is –2.2 and that

$$|-1.7| > \left|\frac{1}{2}\right|$$

because –1.7 is farther from 0 than is 1/2. When students compare absolute values, they should be aware that they are comparing distances from 0. Students can apply this knowledge of comparison to order sets of three or more rational numbers and absolute values, for example, –2.3 < –1/2 < 1/2 and $|-16| > |4| > |-2.2|$.

Rational number operations and properties

In previous grades, students learned how to add, subtract, multiply, and divide whole numbers, positive fractions, and positive decimals. They learned to understand addition as joining and subtraction as the inverse of addition. They learned to understand multiplication as "*n*" groups of "*m*" and division as the inverse of multiplication. As students study rational numbers, their understanding of these operations deepens.

Reflect As You Read

Before you read this section, think about properties of numbers that are true for rational numbers but not true for the set of whole numbers. Use counterexamples to show when a property is not true.

An important part of a curriculum focused on understanding the rational numbers as a system is the property of closure for the different operations. Through classroom discussions, teachers should help students understand this property. For a set of numbers to be closed with respect to an operation, the answer to the computation must be a number in that set. For example, the set of whole numbers is closed with respect to addition because the sum of any two whole numbers is another whole number. The set of whole numbers is also closed with respect to multiplication because the product of any two whole numbers is another whole number. Similarly, the set of rational numbers is closed with respect to addition and multiplication.

Rather than focus on the term *closure*, teachers should focus students' thinking on the reasoning needed to understand the idea of closure. Students can test these properties with specific pairs of numbers, or they can try to think of a pair of rational numbers whose sum or product would *not* be another rational number. In particular, students can explore the idea of closure with an operation and a set of numbers where closure does not exist. For example, teachers can discuss with students how to evaluate such expressions as 6 – 4 and 4 – 6. Students will begin to see that the difference of two whole numbers is not always a whole number. For example, for 4 – 6, there is no whole number that can be added to 6 to get 4. Since negative numbers are needed for the set of whole numbers to be closed under subtraction, and there are no negative whole numbers, the set of whole numbers is not closed with respect to subtraction.

Students should engage in similar reasoning about division—for example, with such expressions as 6 ÷ 3 and 3 ÷ 6. Again, students can begin to see that the quotient of two whole numbers is not always a whole number. In the case of 3 ÷ 6, there is no whole number that can be multiplied by 6 to get 3. Since fractions are needed for the set of whole numbers to be closed under division, except for division by 0, and there are no fractions in the set of whole numbers, the set of whole numbers is not closed with respect to division.

Discussions about the idea of closure can help students understand the uses and power of the rational number system. Students can begin to appreciate that the rational number system has more properties that apply because it contains different kinds of numbers. The set of rational numbers can be used to better represent more situations and solve more problems both within mathematics and in connection with the real world.

Other properties like closure for addition and multiplication exist in both the system of whole numbers and the system of rational numbers. And, as with closure for subtraction and division, some properties exist in the system of rational numbers but not in the system of whole numbers. The commutative property of addition, $a + b = b + a$, is true in both systems, for example, $4 + 5 = 5 + 4$ and $-1.3 + -3/13 = -3/13 + (-1.3)$. Another property that exists in both number systems is the associative property of multiplication,

$$a \times (b \times c) = (a \times b) \times c,$$

for example,

$$8 \times (3 \times 2) = (8 \times 3) \times 2$$

and

$$-\frac{3}{4} \times \left(-5 \times \frac{2}{5}\right) = \left(-\frac{3}{4} \times -5\right) \times \frac{2}{5}.$$

However, the additive inverse property exists for the set of rational numbers but not for the set of whole numbers. The additive inverse property states that for every rational number q, there is a rational number that is the opposite of q, written as $-q$, such that $q + -q = -q + q = 0$; that is, 4 and -4 are additive inverses because $4 + (-4) = -4 + 4 = 0$, and $-1/8$ and $1/8$ are additive inverses because $-1/8 + 1/8 = 1/8 + -1/8 = 0$. Students should be led to reason that, since the additive inverse of a positive number is a negative number, and negative numbers do not exist in the system of whole numbers, the additive inverse property does not exist in the whole-number system. Another property that exists in the rational number system but not in the whole-number system is the multiplicative inverse property, which states that for every rational number q $(q \neq 0)$, there exists a rational number $1/q$ such that

$$q \times \frac{1}{q} = \frac{1}{q} \times q = 1.$$

For example, 7 and 1/7 are multiplicative inverses because $7 \times 1/7 = 1/7 \times 7 = 1$, and $-(3/4)$ and $-(4/3)$ are multiplicative inverses because $-(3/4) \times -(4/3) = -(4/3) \times -(3/4) = 1$. The multiplicative inverse property does not exist in the system of whole numbers because the multiplicative inverse of a whole number is not a whole number. The table in figure 4.4 summarizes and compares some of the important properties of the system of whole numbers and the system of rational numbers.

Computation in the rational number system

After gaining an understanding of what rational numbers are, how to order and compare them, the meaning of absolute value and opposite, and some properties of the rational number system, students are ready to expand their prior understandings of computational procedures for addition, subtraction, multiplication, and division to include the negative numbers. Teachers should point out the similarities and differences of the computational procedures in

Property	Examples from the Whole-Number System	Examples from the Rational Number System
Closure for Addition For any two numbers in the set, their sum is in the set.	For $2 + 5 = n$, $n = 7$ and 7 is a whole number.	For $18.9 + -0.9 = q$, $q = 18$ and 18 is a rational number.
Closure for Multiplication For any two numbers in the set, their product is in the set.	For $2 \times 5 = n$, $n = 10$ and 10 is a whole number.	For $7 \times -3 = q$, $q = -21$ and -21 is a rational number.
Commutative Property of Addition: $a + b = b + a$	$4 + 1 = 1 + 4$	$-6.1 + 0.5 = 0.5 + (-6.1)$
Commutative Property of Multiplication: $ab = ba$	$6 \times 5 = 5 \times 6$	$\frac{3}{8}\left(-\frac{1}{4}\right) = \left(-\frac{1}{4}\right)\left(\frac{3}{8}\right)$
Associative Property of Addition: $(a + b) + c = a + (b + c)$	$(1 + 20) + 2 = 1 + (20 + 2)$	$\left(-3 + \frac{2}{3}\right) + \left(\frac{1}{4}\right) = -3 + \left(\frac{2}{3} + \frac{1}{4}\right)$
Associative Property of Multiplication: $(ab)c = a(bc)$	$(3 \cdot 5) \cdot 8 = 3 \cdot (5 \cdot 8)$	$(1.5 \times 4) \times 0.1 = 1.5 \times (4 \times 0.1)$
Distributive Property of Multiplication over Addition: $a(b + c) = ab + ac$	$2(3 + 4) = 2 \cdot 3 + 2 \cdot 4$	$0.5[1 + (-4)] = (0.5)(1) + (0.5)(-4)$
Distributive Property of Multiplication over Subtraction: $a(b - c) = ab - ac$	$2(8 - 5) = 2 \cdot 8 - 2 \cdot 5$	$\frac{1}{2}\left(-1 - \left(-\frac{2}{3}\right)\right) = \frac{1}{2}(-1) - \frac{1}{2}\left(-\frac{2}{3}\right)$
Additive Identity: $a + 0 = 0 + a = a$	$5 + 0 = 0 + 5 = 5$	$\frac{1}{2} + 0 = 0 + \frac{1}{2} = \frac{1}{2}$
Multiplicative Identity; $1 \times a = a \times 1 = a$	$1 \times 3 = 3 \times 1 = 3$	$\left(-\frac{5}{2}\right)1 = 1\left(-\frac{5}{2}\right) = -\frac{5}{2}$
Multiplicative Property of 0: $0 \times a = a \times 0 = 0$	$0 \times 3 = 3 \times 0 = 0$	$0 \times -\frac{5}{2} = -\frac{5}{2} \times 0 = 0$
Property	**Justifications for Not Existing in the Whole-Number System**	**Examples from the Rational Number System**
Closure for Subtraction For any two numbers in the set, their difference is in the set.	For $5 - 7 = n$, there is no whole number, n, such that $n + 7 = 5$.	$5 - 7 = -2$, -2 is a rational number.
Closure for Division For any two numbers in the set (as long as the divisor is not 0), their quotient is in the set.	For $5 \div 7 = n$, there is no whole number, n, such that $n \times 7 = 5$.	$5 \div 7 = \frac{5}{7}$, $\frac{5}{7}$ is a rational number.

(Continued on next page)

Fig. 4.4. Some properties of whole numbers and rational numbers

Property	Justifications for Not Existing in the Whole-Number System	Examples from the Rational Number System
Additive Inverse Every number a in the set has an additive inverse $-a$ in the set (also called its *opposite*) such that $a + (-a) = (-a + a) = 0$. [Note that 0 is the additive identity.]	There is no whole number n such that $4 + n = 0$.	$\frac{1}{2}$ and $-\frac{1}{2}$ are additive inverses because $\frac{1}{2} + \left(-\frac{1}{2}\right) = -\frac{1}{2} + \frac{1}{2} = 0$.
Multiplicative Inverse Every number a in the set, except 0, has a multiplicative inverse $\frac{1}{a}$ in the set (also called reciprocal) such that $a \cdot \frac{1}{a} = 1$. [Note that 1 is the multiplicative identity.]	The reciprocal of 4 is $\frac{1}{4}$, and $\frac{1}{4}$ is not a whole number.	The reciprocal of -2 is $-\frac{1}{2}$, and $-2\left(-\frac{1}{2}\right) = 1$.
Multiplication Property of –1 $-1a = -a$	$-1 \cdot 4 = -4$; neither -1 nor -4 is a whole number.	$-1\left(-\frac{5}{2}\right) = \frac{5}{2}$

Fig. 4.4. Some properties of whole numbers and rational numbers—*Continued*

the whole-number system and in the rational number system. In initial experiences with computation with negative numbers, teachers should have students use integers. Once students understand the procedures for computing with integers, they can use their previous knowledge of computation with positive fractions and decimals coupled with their new understanding of the procedures for computation with integers to add, subtract, multiply, and divide with all rational numbers.

Adding and subtracting rational numbers

Teachers should help students begin to develop fluency in computation across the entire set of rational numbers by starting with integers to represent situations involving owing (or debt), temperatures below zero, elevation, and so on. Students should be able to use various models to represent integers. This progression is shown in the following classroom discussion about the problem "You owe your brother $7. How can you use integers to represent your debt?"

Teacher: You can use negative numbers to represent an amount owed. If you owe $7, you can think of that as you having –7 dollars. How can you model –7? I see that some students made different models. Mark, can you explain your model?

Mark: I made a number-line model. I started at 0 and then moved 7 units left to plot –7.

Teacher: That makes sense, Mark. Jessica, can you explain your model?

Jessica: I made an algebra tile model. I used 7 negative-one tiles to represent –7. They are kind of like IOU notes, like we use when we play Monopoly and someone runs out of money and wants to keep playing.

Teacher: So, Jessica, how is your model like Mark's model?

Jessica: I have a negative-one tile for every unit that Mark moved to the left of 0.

Hank: I used two-sided counters and used the green side to show negative numbers. Each green counter is –1, so I used seven green counters to show –7. It is a lot like Jessica's model.

Once students understand how to represent situations such as "owing" with negative numbers and can model negative numbers in a variety of ways, the teacher can introduce a simple problem-solving context that students can model with integers, as shown in the continuation of the classroom discussion.

Teacher: If you don't have any other money, and you owe your brother $7, you can think of yourself as having a "net worth" of –7 dollars. Suppose you earn $4. How can you use integers to write a numerical expression that shows your net worth now?

Mark: I owed 7 dollars, so I had –7 dollars. Then I earned $4, so it is like I added 4 to what I was worth. I represented that as –7 + 4.

Teacher: I understand. Did anyone write a different expression?

Lee: I thought of it in a different way. I thought that when I got those 4 dollars, I would give them to my brother right away, which would be like subtracting 4 dollars of debt from my total debt, so I wrote –7 – (–4).

Teacher: Interesting. Actually, the expressions –7 + 4 and –7 – (–4) represent the same relationship. Negatives and positives in mathematics work very much like negatives and positives in language. If you put two negative words together, they make the sentence positive. For example, if I say, "I do not *not* have a dog," what I mean is that I *do* have a dog. It is the same in mathematics. If you subtract a negative number, it is like adding a positive number. You are taking away a negative amount, which is like adding a positive amount.

Once teachers have given students opportunities to model situations using integer expressions, they can lead students one step further to writing and solving equations using integers. Again, students should explore various ways to model integer equations and use the models to solve them, as is evidenced in the continuation of the preceding classroom discussion.

Teacher: Suppose you don't have any money to start with, you owe your brother $7, and you earn $4 that you pay back to him. What is your net worth now? Are you still in debt? We can use the expressions that Mark and Lee wrote to write equations to represent the situation. With Mark's expression, the equation would be $-7 + 4 = x$. With Lee's expression, the equation would be $-7 - (-4) = x$. Let's use models to show how to solve the equations. Using Mark's model, let's draw an arrow 7 units long to the left of 0 to represent -7. His equation is $-7 + 4 = x$. To show adding 4, we can draw an arrow from -7 that is 4 units to the right to represent adding a positive 4. Label it $+ 4$ to indicate adding 4. The value of x is the point on which we land. What is the value of x? [$x = -3$] So $-7 + 4 = -3$.

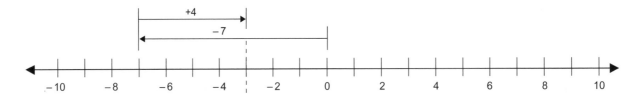

Now let's use Jessica's algebra tiles to model $-7 + 4 = x$. To show adding 4, place 4 positive-one tiles below the 7 negative-one tiles.

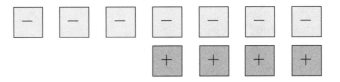

One positive-one tile and one negative-one tile make a "zero pair" because they are additive inverses: $+1 + (-1) = 0$. You can circle the zero pairs to show that those pairs of tiles combine to make a value of zero. The tiles that are left show the value of x.

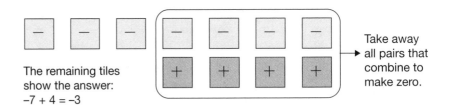

The remaining tiles show the answer:
$-7 + 4 = -3$

Take away all pairs that combine to make zero.

Now let's use algebra tiles to model Lee's equation, $-7 - (-4) = x$. To show subtracting -4 with algebra tiles, you need to take away four negative-one tiles. The tiles that are left show the answer.

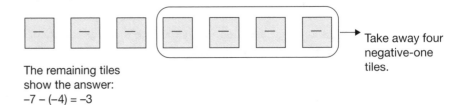

The remaining tiles show the answer:
$-7 - (-4) = -3$

Take away four negative-one tiles.

Notice that –7 + 4 = *x* and –7 – (–4) = *x* both have the same solution, *x* = –3. Your net worth is now –3 dollars; since the 3 is negative, you owe 3 dollars.

Students should have many opportunities to represent, model, and solve problems using equations and integers. Through modeling integers in meaningful situations, students can build a deeper understanding of efficient, accurate, and generalizable methods for adding and subtracting with integers. Several examples of models are provided in figure 4.5. Although a number line also can be used to model subtracting negative numbers, the counter or algebra tile models may be more intuitive for students.

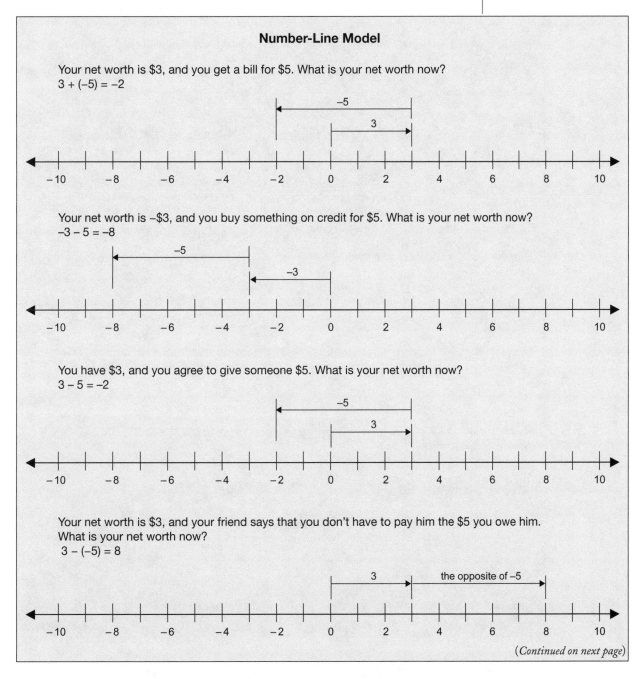

(*Continued on next page*)

Fig. 4.5. Models showing addition and subtraction with integers

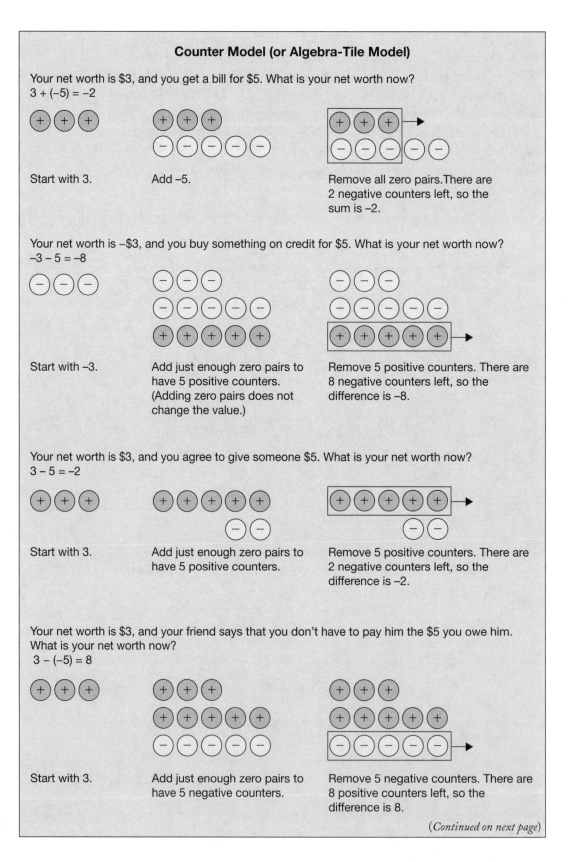

Counter Model (or Algebra-Tile Model)

Your net worth is $3, and you get a bill for $5. What is your net worth now?
3 + (−5) = −2

Start with 3.

Add −5.

Remove all zero pairs. There are 2 negative counters left, so the sum is −2.

Your net worth is −$3, and you buy something on credit for $5. What is your net worth now?
−3 − 5 = −8

Start with −3.

Add just enough zero pairs to have 5 positive counters. (Adding zero pairs does not change the value.)

Remove 5 positive counters. There are 8 negative counters left, so the difference is −8.

Your net worth is $3, and you agree to give someone $5. What is your net worth now?
3 − 5 = −2

Start with 3.

Add just enough zero pairs to have 5 positive counters.

Remove 5 positive counters. There are 2 negative counters left, so the difference is −2.

Your net worth is $3, and your friend says that you don't have to pay him the $5 you owe him. What is your net worth now?
3 − (−5) = 8

Start with 3.

Add just enough zero pairs to have 5 negative counters.

Remove 5 negative counters. There are 8 positive counters left, so the difference is 8.

(Continued on next page)

Fig. 4.5. Models showing addition and subtraction with integers—*Continued*

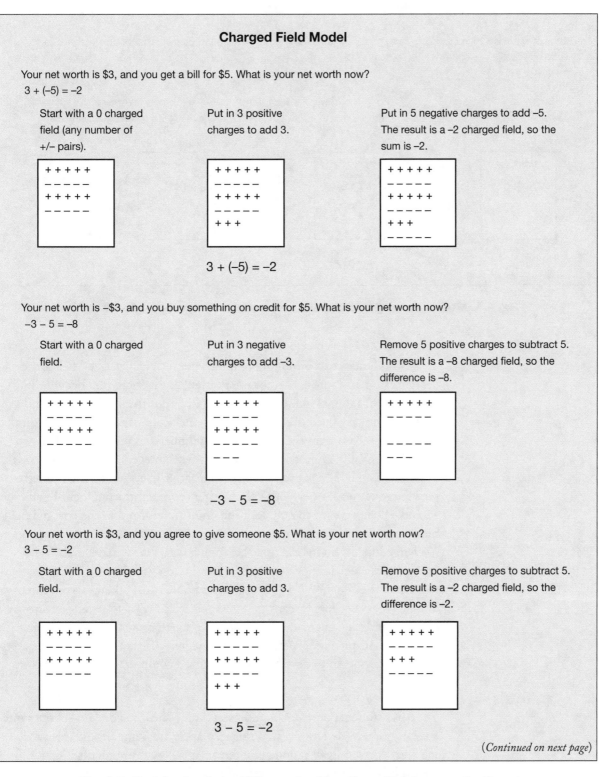

Charged Field Model

Your net worth is $3, and you get a bill for $5. What is your net worth now?
3 + (–5) = –2

| Start with a 0 charged field (any number of +/– pairs). | Put in 3 positive charges to add 3. | Put in 5 negative charges to add –5. The result is a –2 charged field, so the sum is –2. |

3 + (–5) = –2

Your net worth is –$3, and you buy something on credit for $5. What is your net worth now?
–3 – 5 = –8

| Start with a 0 charged field. | Put in 3 negative charges to add –3. | Remove 5 positive charges to subtract 5. The result is a –8 charged field, so the difference is –8. |

–3 – 5 = –8

Your net worth is $3, and you agree to give someone $5. What is your net worth now?
3 – 5 = –2

| Start with a 0 charged field. | Put in 3 positive charges to add 3. | Remove 5 positive charges to subtract 5. The result is a –2 charged field, so the difference is –2. |

3 – 5 = –2

(Continued on next page)

Fig. 4.5. Models showing addition and subtraction with integers—*Continued*

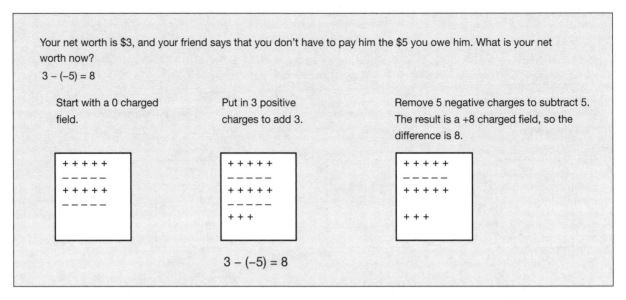

Your net worth is $3, and your friend says that you don't have to pay him the $5 you owe him. What is your net worth now?

3 – (–5) = 8

| Start with a 0 charged field. | Put in 3 positive charges to add 3. | Remove 5 negative charges to subtract 5. The result is a +8 charged field, so the difference is 8. |

3 – (–5) = 8

Fig. 4.5. Models showing addition and subtraction with integers—*Continued*

As students work with number lines, counters, and charged fields, they begin to gain an appreciation for the special nature of the number zero in the system of rational numbers. Zero is neither positive nor negative, and it separates the set of positive numbers from the set of negative numbers on the number line. Also, zero is the sum of any number and its opposite. This fact is used extensively in models of operations with integers, in which zero pairs, a combination of a "positive one" and a "negative one," can be used to represent the equation $1 + (–1) = 0$. When using counters, any number of pairs of +1 and –1 can be used to represent the number zero, and in the charged field model, any number of +/– pairs can be used in the field to represent a "0 charged field." So for example, beginning with 10 +/– pairs in the field represents the equation $10 + (–10) = 0$, beginning with 8 +/– pairs in the field represents the equation $8 + (–8) = 0$, and so on. During their exploration of integer models, students learn that many different ways to represent zero are possible, and they understand zero to mean much more than just "nothing."

Through students' experiences with modeling integer addition and subtraction, they begin to develop the generalized computation rules, as shown in figure 4.6.

After students develop an understanding of how to add and subtract integers, they are ready to learn that they can apply the same procedures for adding and subtracting all rational numbers. At this point, students in grade 7 are ready to connect their understandings of how to add and subtract positive decimals and fractions and how to add and subtract integers to extend their computational skills to include adding and subtracting negative fractions and decimals. Examples of the types of rational number expressions that students should be able to evaluate are shown in figure 4.7.

Adding Integers	
Rule	**Examples**
To add two integers that have the same sign: Add the absolute values. Use the sign of the addends.	$3 + 5 = 8$ $-3 + (-5) = -8$
To add two integers that have different signs: Subtract the lesser absolute value from the greater absolute value. Use the sign of the addend that has the greater absolute value.	$3 + (-5) = -2$ $-3 + 5 = 2$
The sum of any integer and its opposite is zero.	$6 + (-6) = 0$ $-1 + 1 = 0$

Subtracting Integers	
Rule	**Examples**
To subtract an integer, add its opposite.	$3 - 5 = 3 + (-5) = -2$ $3 - (-5) = 3 + 5 = 8$

Fig. 4.6. Rules for adding and subtracting integers

Addition Examples	
$-\dfrac{1}{2} + -\dfrac{1}{4}$	The signs are the same. $\dfrac{1}{2} + \dfrac{1}{4} = \dfrac{3}{4}$ ← First, add the absolute values. $-\dfrac{1}{2} + -\dfrac{1}{4} = -\dfrac{3}{4}$ ← Then use the sign of the numbers.
$3.2 + 1.06$	The signs are the same. $3.2 + 1.06 = 4.26$ ← First, add the absolute values. $3.2 + 1.06 = 4.26$ ← Then use the sign of the numbers.
$1 + (-80)$	The signs are different. $80 - 1 = 79$ ← First, subtract the lesser absolute value from the greater absolute value. $1 + (-80) = -79$ ← Use the sign of the number that has the greater absolute value.
$-4\dfrac{3}{5} + \dfrac{1}{10}$	The signs are different. $4\dfrac{3}{5} - \dfrac{1}{10} = 4\dfrac{5}{10} = 4\dfrac{1}{2}$ ← Subtract the lesser absolute value from the greater absolute value. $-4\dfrac{3}{5} + \dfrac{1}{10} = -4\dfrac{1}{2}$ ← Use the sign of the number that has the greater absolute value. *(Continued on next page)*

Fig. 4.7. Examples of addition and subtraction with rational numbers

Addition Examples	
$-\dfrac{3}{8}+\dfrac{3}{8}$	$-\dfrac{3}{8}+\dfrac{3}{8}=0 \leftarrow$ The sum of any number and its opposite is zero.
Subtraction Practice Examples **To subtract a rational number, add its opposite.**	
$20-50$	$20-50=20+(-50)=-30$
$20-(-50)$	$20-(-50)=20+50=70$
$-0.4-(-1.1)$	$-0.4-(-1.1)=-0.4+1.1=0.7$
$-\dfrac{2}{3}-\dfrac{5}{6}$	$\begin{aligned} -\dfrac{2}{3}-\dfrac{5}{6} &= -\dfrac{2}{3}+\left(-\dfrac{5}{6}\right) \\[4pt] &= -\dfrac{4}{6}+\left(-\dfrac{5}{6}\right) \\[4pt] &= -\dfrac{9}{6} \\[4pt] &= -1\dfrac{3}{6} \\[4pt] &= -1\dfrac{1}{2} \end{aligned}$

Fig. 4.7. Examples of addition and subtraction with rational numbers—*Continued*

Reflect As You Read

Prior to reading this section, think about how you explain to your students the rules for multiplying and dividing integers so that the rules make sense.

Multiplying and dividing integers

After learning how to add and subtract rational numbers, students are ready to learn how to multiply and divide rational numbers. As with addition and subtraction, it is beneficial for students to apply what they know about multiplicative relationships with whole numbers to explore multiplicative relationships using integers. Then they can generalize their understandings to all rational numbers.

There are several ways to show students the results of multiplying with integers. One way is to explore patterns, as shown in figure 4.8.

2 × 3 = 6	6 × 3 = 18
2 × 2 = 4	6 × 2 = 12
2 × 1 = 2	6 × 1 = 6
2 × 0 = 0	6 × 0 = 0
2 × (−1) = −2	6 × (−1) = −6
2 × (−2) = −4	6 × (−2) = −12
2 × (−3) = −6	6 × (−3) = −18

Fig. 4.8. Examples that show how to use patterns to explore multiplication of integers

As students experience more and more of these carefully constructed patterns, they begin to see that if you multiply a positive number by a positive number, you get a positive number. If you multiply a positive number by a negative number, you get a negative number. During classroom discussions about multiplication of integers, a teacher can point out that it is difficult to model "negative 2" groups, so students can use the patterns they developed along with their understanding of the commutative property to suggest a rule for multiplying a negative number times a positive number. For example, a teacher might explain that students saw from the pattern that $2 \times (-3) = -6$. Also, they know from the commutative property of multiplication that $2 \times (-3) = (-3) \times 2$, so it is true that $(-3) \times 2 = -6$. Teachers can extend students' understanding by having students use what they know about opposites to suggest a rule for multiplying a negative number times a negative number. For example, a teacher might explain that, from the pattern, students saw that $2 \times (-3) = -6$. Also, students know that -2 is the opposite of 2 and 6 is the opposite of -6, so it make sense that $-2 \times (-3)$ is the opposite of $2 \times (-3)$, and $-2 \times (-3) = 6$.

Teachers can also use various models to represent multiplication of integers. One such representation involves the charged field model. In the charged field model, as shown in figure 4.9, if the number of groups is positive, you put in either positive or negative charges. If the number of groups is negative, you take out either positive or negative charges. If the number in each group is positive, you either put in or take out positive charges. If the number in each group is negative, you either put in or take out negative charges.

After students have learned about and understand the rules for multiplying integers, they can use what they know about the mathematical relationship between multiplication and division to discover the rules for dividing integers. Specifically, they can think of division problems as multiplication problems with missing factors, as shown in figure 4.10.

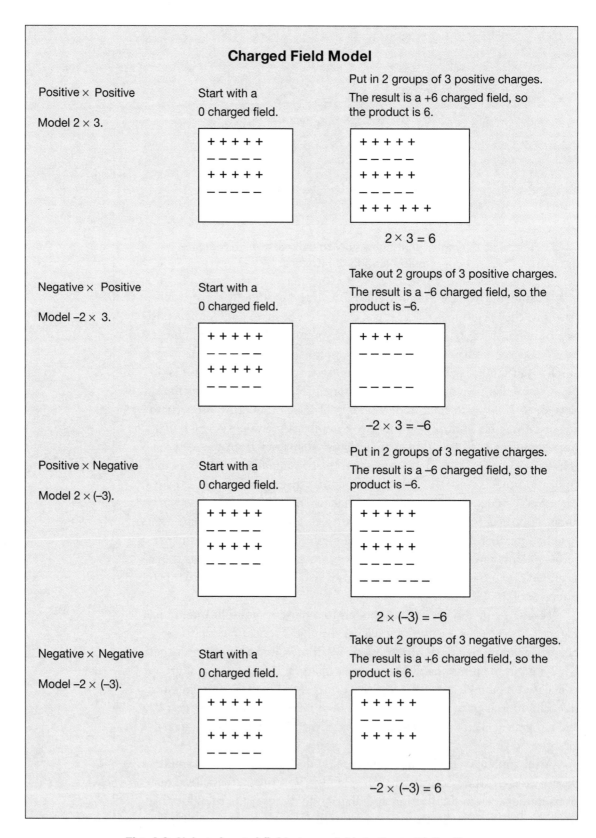

Fig. 4.9. Using charged fields to model integer multiplication

Division Problem	Corresponding Missing-Factor Problem
Positive ÷ positive 12 ÷ 3 = ? $\longrightarrow$	? × 3 = 12 → 4 × 3 = 12, so 12 ÷ 3 = 4.
Positive ÷ negative 12 ÷ (–3) = ? $\longrightarrow$	? × (–3) = 12 → –4 × (–3) = 12, so 12 ÷ (–3) = –4.
Negative ÷ positive –12 ÷ 3 = ? $\longrightarrow$	? × 3 = –12 → –4 × 3 = –12, so –12 ÷ 3 = –4.
Negative ÷ negative –12 ÷ (–3) = ? $\longrightarrow$	? × (–3) = –12 → 4 × (–3) = –12, so –12 ÷ (–3) = 4.

Fig. 4.10. How to use multiplication to divide integers

Teachers should help students by explaining that they should ask themselves questions, such as in the example 12 ÷ (–3), "What times –3 will equal 12?" If students have developed a thorough understanding of the rules for multiplying integers, they will realize that –4 × –3 = 12, and so 12 ÷ (–3) = –4.

Through carefully structured experiences, students can learn the related rules for multiplying and dividing integers, which are summarized in figure 4.11.

Rules for Multiplying and Dividing Integers	
positive × positive = positive	positive ÷ positive = positive
positive × negative = negative	positive ÷ negative = negative
negative × positive = negative	negative ÷ positive = negative
negative × negative = positive	negative ÷ negative = positive

Fig. 4.11. Rules for multiplying and dividing integers

Students should be encouraged to summarize the rules for multiplication and division of one integer by another: "When the signs are the same, the answer is positive. When the signs are different, the answer is negative." Teachers should also point out that the product of any number and zero is zero, and zero is neither positive nor negative. Also, students can use the definition of division to confirm that if you divide zero by any rational number other than zero, the quotient is zero (i.e., when $q \neq 0$, $0 \div q = 0$ because $0 \times q = 0$) and that dividing by zero is undefined (i.e., for $r \neq 0$, $r \div 0$ is undefined because there is no rational number that you can multiply by 0 to get a nonzero r). Note that students might reason that the quotient $0 \div 0$ is 0 because $0 \times 0 = 0$; however, if the quotient $0 \div 0 = n$ existed, n could be *any* rational number, since any number times 0 equals 0. Therefore, $0 \div 0$ is undefined because an infinite number of answers are possible.

After students develop an understanding of how to multiply and divide integers, they are ready to learn that they can apply the same procedures for multiplying and dividing all rational numbers (except for division by 0). At this point, students in grade 7 are ready to connect their understandings of how to multiply and divide positive decimals and fractions and how to multiply and divide integers to extend their computational skills to include multiplying and dividing negative fractions and decimals. Examples of the types of rational number expressions that students should be able to evaluate are shown in figure 4.12.

Percent as a fraction or decimal

In grade 7, students develop an understanding of percent as a part-to-whole ratio where n percent means n parts out of 100 total parts. The word *percent* means hundredths, out of a hundred, or per hundred. Since a ratio can be represented with a fraction, percents can be represented with fractions and as decimals. In previous grades, students have explored equivalent fractions and decimals. Specifically, they learned to write a fraction in the form

$$\frac{a}{b}$$

as an equivalent terminating or repeating decimal by using division, and they learned to write a terminating decimal as an equivalent fraction in the form

$$\frac{a}{b}.$$

In grade 7, they extend this understanding to include flexible translation among equivalent percent, fraction, and decimal forms. For example, a student who knows that 34 percent means 34 out of 100 should be able to use her or his understanding of rational numbers and ratios to reason that

$$34\% = \frac{34}{100} = 0.34$$

and

$$34\% = \frac{34}{100} = \frac{17}{50}.$$

Hundredths grid models can help students connect percent, fraction, and decimal notation, as shown in figure 4.13.

	Multiplication and Division Practice Examples Multiply or divide as if the numbers were both positive. Determine the sign, and write the answer.
-10×224	$10 \times 224 = 2240 \quad \leftarrow$ Multiply. $-10 \times 224 = -2240 \leftarrow$ Write the sign. Negative $\times$ positive = negative.
$\left(-\dfrac{1}{2}\right)\left(-\dfrac{1}{4}\right)$	$\left(\dfrac{1}{2}\right)\left(\dfrac{1}{4}\right) = \dfrac{1}{8} \leftarrow$ Multiply. $\left(-\dfrac{1}{2}\right)\left(-\dfrac{1}{4}\right) = \dfrac{1}{8} \leftarrow$ Write the sign. Negative $\times$ negative = positive.
$\left(3\dfrac{1}{2}\right)\left(-\dfrac{1}{7}\right)$	$3\dfrac{1}{2} \times \dfrac{1}{7} = \dfrac{7}{2} \times \dfrac{1}{7} = \dfrac{1}{2} \quad \leftarrow$ Multiply. $3\dfrac{1}{2} \times -\dfrac{1}{7} = -\dfrac{1}{2} \qquad\qquad \leftarrow$ Write the sign. Positive $\times$ negative = negative.
$1.24 \div (-4)$	$\begin{array}{r} 0.31 \\ 4\overline{)1.24} \end{array} \qquad\qquad \leftarrow$ Divide. $1.24 \div (-4) = -0.31 \leftarrow$ Write the sign. Positive $\div$ negative = negative.
$\left(-\dfrac{1}{2}\right) \div \left(-2\dfrac{1}{2}\right)$	$\left(\dfrac{1}{2}\right) \div \left(2\dfrac{1}{2}\right) = \left(\dfrac{1}{2}\right) \div \left(\dfrac{5}{2}\right) = \left(\dfrac{1}{2}\right) \times \left(\dfrac{2}{5}\right) = \dfrac{1}{5} \leftarrow$ Divide. $\left(-\dfrac{1}{2}\right) \div \left(-2\dfrac{1}{2}\right) = \dfrac{1}{5} \qquad\qquad \leftarrow$ Write the sign. $\qquad\qquad\qquad\qquad\qquad\qquad$ Negative $\div$ negative = positive.

Fig. 4.12. Examples of multiplication and division with rational numbers

As students work with percents, they begin to gain an understanding of a percent of a number. Number lines can aid students in this understanding, as shown in figure 4.14.

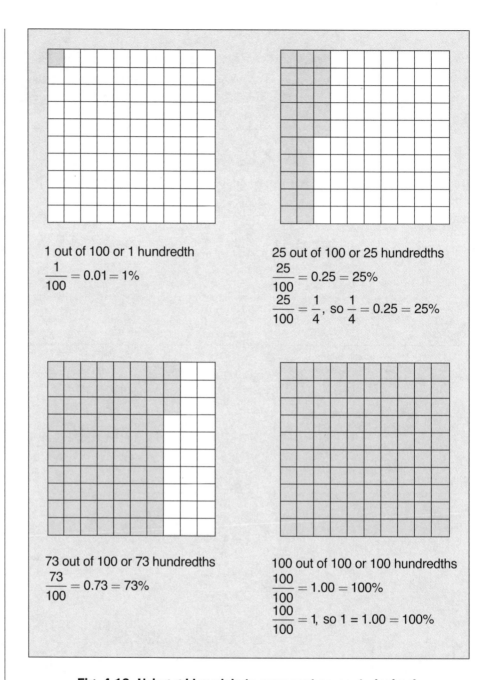

Fig. 4.13. Using grid models to represent percent, decimal, and fraction equivalencies

Students also begin to understand the connections among finding a percent of a number, finding a fraction of a number, and multiplying a number by a decimal. Number lines can also help students gain this understanding, as shown in figure 4.15. Through carefully structured experiences such as these, students begin to develop the understanding of the equivalencies of fractions and decimals that will enable them to convert flexibly from one form of rational number to another.

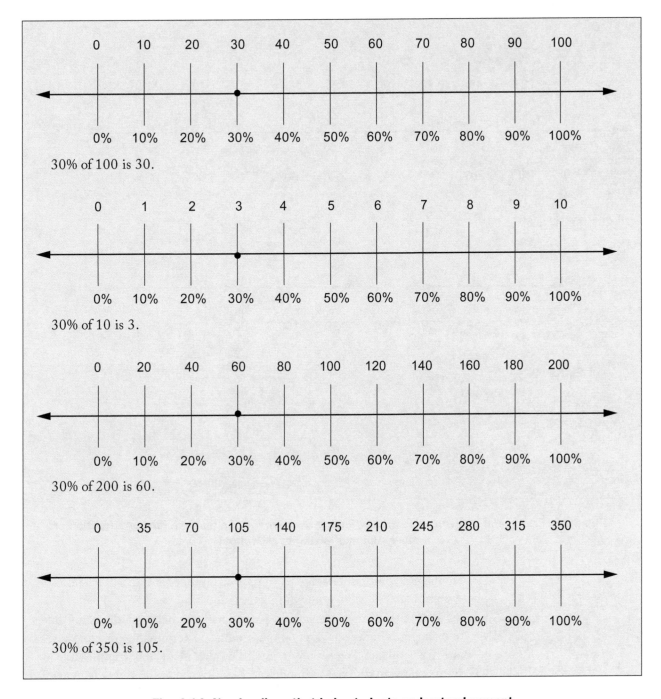

Fig. 4.14. Number lines that help students understand percent

Students should use equivalent fractions, percents, and terminating and repeating decimals to represent rational numbers in a variety of contexts. As they work with these representations, students begin to realize that some decimals are terminating, some are repeating, and some, such as π (pi), are neither repeating nor terminating. Students learn that only terminating and repeating decimals are included in the rational number system, and numbers like π are not included in the rational number system. Experiences with such

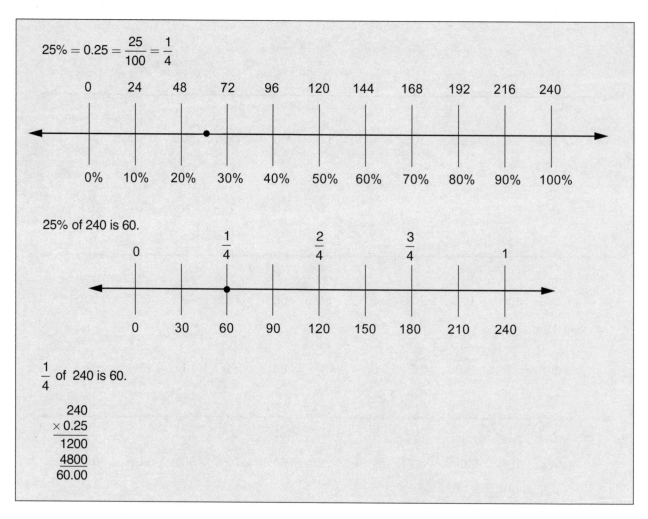

$$25\% = 0.25 = \frac{25}{100} = \frac{1}{4}$$

25% of 240 is 60.

$\frac{1}{4}$ of 240 is 60.

```
   240
 × 0.25
 ──────
  1200
  4800
 ──────
 60.00
```

Fig. 4.15. Example of equivalencies among finding the percent of a number, finding a fraction of a number, and multiplying by a decimal

numbers as π introduce students to irrational numbers and the real number system that they will work with in later grades.

Part of students' understanding of rational numbers includes being able to distinguish between a fraction that results in a terminating decimal and one that results in a repeating decimal. Through many opportunities to convert fractions to decimals using division, students gain the ability to generalize that any fraction in simplest form whose numerator is an integer and whose denominator's prime factorization has prime factors of only 2 and/or 5 has a terminating decimal representation, because denominators with factors of only 2 and/or 5 can be multiplied by the appropriate number of factors of 2 and/or 5 to make pairs of factors of 2 and 5, resulting in powers of 10. For example, 3/20 has a denominator with two factors of 2 and one factor of 5, so 3/20 can be multiplied by 5/5 to make two pairs of factors of 2 and 5, forming the equivalent fraction 15/100, which is equal to 0.15.

Students learn that all the other rational fractions, that is, the fractions in simplest form whose numerators are integers and denominators have prime factors other than 2 or 5, have repeating decimal representations, because those denominators cannot be multiplied by integers to form powers of 10. For example,

$$3/11 = 0.2727\ldots = 0.\overline{27}.$$

Examples of some fractions, the prime factorization of their denominators, and their terminating or repeating decimal equivalents are shown in figure 4.16.

Fraction	Prime Factorization of Denominator In Simplest Form	Equivalent Fraction with Integer Numerator and Denominator That Is a Power of 10	Decimal Equivalent	Repeating/ Terminating
$\dfrac{2}{3}$	3	none	$0.\overline{6}$	Repeating
$\dfrac{9}{12} = \dfrac{3}{4}$	2×2	$\dfrac{3}{4} = \dfrac{3}{2 \times 2} \times \dfrac{5 \times 5}{5 \times 5} = \dfrac{75}{100}$	0.75	Terminating
$\dfrac{3}{5}$	5	$\dfrac{3}{5} = \dfrac{3}{5} \times \dfrac{2}{2} = \dfrac{6}{10}$	0.6	Terminating
$\dfrac{5}{6}$	2×3	none	$0.8\overline{3}$	Repeating
$\dfrac{15}{24} = \dfrac{5}{8}$	$2 \times 2 \times 2$	$\dfrac{5}{8} = \dfrac{5}{2 \times 2 \times 2} \times \dfrac{5 \times 5 \times 5}{5 \times 5 \times 5} = \dfrac{625}{1000}$	0.625	Terminating
$\dfrac{7}{9}$	3×3	none	$.\overline{7}$	Repeating
$\dfrac{3}{10}$	2×5	$\dfrac{3}{10} = \dfrac{3}{2 \times 5} = \dfrac{3}{10}$	0.3	Terminating
$\dfrac{2}{11}$	11	none	$0.1\overline{8}$	Repeating
$\dfrac{7}{12}$	$2 \times 2 \times 3$	none	$.58\overline{3}$	Repeating
$\dfrac{11}{25}$	5×5	$\dfrac{11}{25} = \dfrac{11}{5 \times 5} \times \dfrac{2 \times 2}{2 \times 2} = \dfrac{44}{100}$	0.44	Terminating

Fig. 4.16. Examples of how to determine if a rational number has a terminating or repeating decimal representation

Equations and rational numbers

In grade 7 students apply both their understanding of the properties of rational numbers and their computational skills to solve equations. They then apply these skills as they use equations to solve problems.

In grade 6, students learned about the equality properties of addition, subtraction, multiplication, and division. For example, they learned that they can divide both sides of an equation by the same nonzero number and create an equivalent equation, that is, $42 = 6x$ is equivalent to $42/6 = x$ because you can divide both sides of the equation by 6 and still maintain the same solution. They also learned that if two equations are equivalent, a solution to one equation is a solution to the other equation. Using the previous example, if $x = 7$ is a solution to the equation $42/6 = x$, it is also the solution to the equation $42 = 6x$. Students can test this result by substitution:

$$42 = 6x \qquad \frac{42}{6} = x$$
$$42 = 6(7) \qquad \frac{42}{6} = 7$$
$$42 = 42 \qquad\qquad 7 = 7$$

Although students have solved equations with one variable in previous mathematical experiences, in grade 7 they learn to apply the properties of rational numbers, specifically the multiplicative inverse property and the additive inverse property, to solve equations. Consider the example $25 = x + 15$. The additive inverse property states that the sum of a number and its additive inverse is 0. A step in solving some equations is to create an equivalent equation of the form $x = $ _____. Since 15 is added to x, students learn that they can write an equivalent equation by adding the additive inverse of 15, –15, to both sides of the equation to get the following:

$$25 = x + 15$$
$$25 + (-15) = x + 15 + (-15)$$
$$10 = x + 0$$
$$10 = x$$

In grade 7 students begin to make the connection that subtracting a number is the same as adding the opposite of the number. The solutions in Figure 4.17 show this transition.

Subtracting a Number to Solve	Adding the Additive Inverse to Solve
$25 = x + 15$	$25 = x + 15$
$25 - 15 = x + 15 - 15$	$25 + (-15) = x + 15 + (-15)$
$10 = x$	$10 = x$

Fig. 4.17. Transitioning from using subtraction to solve an equation to using the additive inverse

In the same way, students transition from using division to using the multiplicative inverse property to solve equations. The multiplicative inverse property states that if you multiply a number and its multiplicative inverse, in either order, the product is 1. For example, the multiplicative inverse of 6 is 1/6 because 6 × 1/6 = 1. Through carefully constructed examples, students learn that dividing by a number is the same as multiplying a number by its multiplicative inverse, also called its *reciprocal*. For example, 2 and 1/2 are multiplicative inverses, so 6 ÷ 2 = 3 and 6 × 1/2 = 6/2 = 3. This transition can be seen in the example in figure 4.18.

Dividing by a Number to Solve	Multiplying by the Multiplicative Inverse to Solve
$42 = 6x$ $42 \div 6 = 6x \div 6$ $7 = x$	$42 = 6x$ $42 \cdot \dfrac{1}{6} = 6 \cdot \dfrac{1}{6} x$ $7 = x$

Fig. 4.18. Transitioning from using division to solve an equation to using the multiplicative inverse

As students begin using the multiplicative inverse property to solve equations, they should also begin to transition to thinking of, for example, $3x$ as $(3/1)x$ and $x/3$ as $(1/3)x$. Understanding these equivalencies will help prepare students to solve equations involving rational coefficients, such as $(2/3)x$, by multiplying by the multiplicative inverse of 2/3, or 3/2.

Teachers can present students with opportunities to connect their understandings of equations and rational numbers and their properties as illustrated in the following classroom discussion of this problem:

Suppose Joey owes his sister $10. You can think of Joey's net worth as –10 dollars. Then he got some money and used the money to pay back his sister. After paying some of the money back, he still owes $2. How much did he pay back?

Teacher: What equation did you write to represent the problem?
Maria: I wrote $-10 + x = -2$, because Joey started with –10 dollars. Then he got an unknown amount of money, so he added that money to the amount he had, so I wrote $-10 + x$. After he paid the money, he still owed 2 dollars, which is like having –2 dollars, so I wrote the equation $-10 + x = -2$.
Teacher: I see how you got that equation. How would you solve your equation, Maria?
Maria: Well, –10 is added to x, so I would subtract –10 from both sides of the equation.

$$-10 + x = -2$$
$$-10 - (-10) + x = -2 - (-10)$$
$$x = -2 + 10$$
$$x = 8$$

So Joey paid his sister 8 dollars.

Teacher: You used the opposite of addition, subtraction, and the subtraction property of equality. That is one way to find the answer. As I was walking around, I saw that some of you used the equation $-10 + x = -2$ but solved it a different way. Would someone like to explain what they did?

Tabitha: I will. I used the additive inverse. I know that the additive inverse of -10 is $+10$, because $-10 + 10 = 0$. So I added 10 to both sides to solve the equation.

$$-10 + x = -2$$
$$-10 + 10 + x = -2 + 10$$
$$x = 8$$

Teacher: Interesting. Look at what Tabitha and Maria did to solve the equation. One subtracted -10 from both sides. One added 10 to both sides. They both got $x = 8$. That makes sense because when you subtract, you add the opposite, so subtracting -10 is like adding 10. I saw that some of you wrote a different equation. Would anyone like to share another equation that you can use to solve the problem?

Yashi: I used a different equation. I used $-10 - (-x) = -2$. I thought about it like this: Joey started with -10 dollars. When he paid an unknown amount of money, it was like he was subtracting a certain amount of his debt. The amount he subtracted was negative x, so I wrote $-10 - (-x)$. He still had 2 dollars of debt, so $-10 - (-x) = -2$.

Teacher: That is another way to look at the problem. How did you solve the equation?

Yashi: Well, subtracting a negative number is like adding a positive number, and x is a number, so I rewrote the equation as $-10 + x = -2$. Then I solved it using the additive inverses and the equality property of addition like Tabitha.

Teacher: As you can see, understanding that subtracting a negative number is the same as adding a positive number is important when representing and solving problems involving rational numbers in equations.

During discussions such as the previous one, teachers should emphasize that as students solve an equation, they are using properties of equality to write equivalent equations. Each equation in the solution should be equivalent to the equation before and after it.

Equations can be tested for equivalence by having students substitute the solution value for x into each equation, as shown in figure 4.19.

$-10 + x = -2$ $-10 - (-10) + x = -2 - (-10)$ $x = -2 + 10$ $x = 8$	$-10 + 8 = -2$ $-10 - (-10) + 8 = -2 - (-10)$ $8 = -2 + 10$ $8 = 8$
$2x - 10 = 4$ $2x - 10 + 10 = 4 + 10$ $\dfrac{1}{2} \cdot 2x = \dfrac{1}{2} \cdot 14$ $x = 7$	$2(7) - 10 = 4$ $2(7) - 10 + 10 = 4 + 10$ $\dfrac{1}{2} \cdot 2(7) = \dfrac{1}{2} \cdot 14$ $7 = 7$

Fig. 4.19. Example illustrating that solving equations results in a set of equivalent equations

Reflect As You Read

What are the advantages of having students understand multiple equivalent ways to represent the same problem?

After students become proficient with solving simple one-step equations, or equations involving one operation, they can begin to solve two-step equations, or equations involving two operations. Students need to understand the order of operations to solve these equations. They learn that the most generalizable way to solve two-step equations is to apply operations in the opposite order as that used for computing; "undo" the addition or subtraction before "undoing" the multiplication or division. An example of solving a two-step equation is shown in figure 4.20.

Referring to figure 4.20, as students become more familiar with the process of solving equations, they can eventually leave out such equations as $3x + 0 = 5$ and $1x = 5/3$, since they will have developed the understanding of the additive and multiplicative identities: that any number plus 0 is that number and that any number times 1 is that number.

After students have had many experiences solving equations involving integers, teachers should present parallel problems that involve other rational numbers, as shown in figure 4.21. As students solve equations that require more steps, they will need to make strategic choices regarding how to solve the equations to ensure both the accuracy and efficiency of their problem-solving techniques.

$3x - 1 = 4$ ← When computing, the value for x is first multiplied by 3, and then 1 is subtracted from the product. To solve, first "undo" the subtraction, then the multiplication.

$3x - 1 + 1 = 4 + 1$ ← Think of −1 as "adding −1," and use the addition property of equality to add the additive inverse, +1, to both sides of the equation to create an equivalent equation.

$3x + 0 = 5$

$3x = 5$

$\dfrac{1}{3} \times 3x = \dfrac{1}{3} \times 5$ ← Use the multiplicative property of equality to multiply both sides of the equation by the multiplicative inverse of 3, which is 1/3, to create an equivalent equation.

$1x = \dfrac{5}{3}$

$x = \dfrac{5}{3}$

Fig. 4.20. Solving a two-step equation

Problem 1:

The water level in a reservoir is $4\frac{1}{6}$ feet below normal during a drought. After a rain, the water level is $2\frac{3}{4}$ feet below normal. How many feet did the water level rise?

Solution:

$$-4\frac{1}{6} + x = -2\frac{3}{4}$$

$$-4\frac{1}{6} + 4\frac{1}{6} + x = -2\frac{3}{4} + 4\frac{1}{6}$$

$$x = -2\frac{3}{4} + 4\frac{1}{6}$$

$$x = -2\frac{9}{12} + 4\frac{2}{12}$$

$$x = 1\frac{5}{12}$$

The water level rose $1\frac{5}{12}$ feet.

Problem 2:

You buy a pizza and 5 drinks for $20.70. The pizza costs $12.95. Each drink cost the same amount. What is the cost of each drink?

Solution:

$$12.95 + 5x = 20.70$$

$$12.95 + (-12.95) + 5x = 20.70 + (-12.95)$$

$$5x = 7.75$$

$$\frac{1}{5} \times 5x = \frac{1}{5} \times 7.75$$

$$x = 1.55$$

The cost of each drink is $1.55.

Fig. 4.21. Examples of using equations with rational numbers to solve problems

Strengthening Understanding of Rational Numbers through Problem Solving

For students to develop skills for computing with rational numbers and gain an appreciation of the power of the rational number system, they need opportunities to solve problems involving rational numbers. Teachers should structure problem-solving opportunities to highlight relevant concepts, such as the application of additive and multiplicative inverses, properties of equality, and operations with rational numbers.

The problems shown in figure 4.22 are examples of problems that can be used to highlight operations with rational numbers. The problems shown in figure 4.23 are examples of problems that can be used to highlight the properties of equality. The problem shown in figure 4.24 is an example of a problem that can be used to highlight the multiplicative inverse property. Problems involving measurement, like the one shown in figure 4.25, can help students understand how to use the equality properties to write equivalent equations involving rational numbers.

Problem 1:
The temperature was –3° C at night. The temperature dropped 5 degrees next morning. What was the temperature the next morning?

Solution:
$-3 - (5) = -3 + -5 = -8$
The temperature was –8° C.

Problem 2:
Kevin has a savings account. He keeps track of the change in the account balance each month by recording a positive amount for an increase and a negative amount for a decrease. The table shows what Kevin recorded for six months.

Month	January	February	March	April	May	June
Change in Account Balance	+$12.50	–$32.00	–$10.50	+$44.00	–$12.00	–$6.80

What was the average change per month (the mean of the changes)? Was it a decrease or an increase? Show your work.

Solution:
$$\frac{12.50 + (-32) + (-10.50) + 44 + (-12) + (-6.80)}{6} = \frac{-4.8}{6} = -0.80$$
The change was a decrease of $0.80 per month.

Fig. 4.22. Examples of problems that highlight operations with rational numbers

Problem 1:

Amanda earns $7.80 per hour. One week she earned $128.70. How many hours did she work?

Solution:

$7.80x = 128.70$ ← Let x represent the number of hours.

$\dfrac{7.80x}{7.80} = \dfrac{128.70}{7.80}$ ← Use the division property of equality.

$x = 16.5$

Amanda worked 16.5 hours.

Problem 1:

You have $30. You want to buy a shirt for $16.95 and as many pairs of socks as possible for $2.35 per pair. How many pairs of socks can you buy? Write and solve an equation to solve the problem. State what your variable represents. Identify the properties you use. If the solution to your equation is not the answer to the problem, explain why.

Solution:

$16.95 + 2.35x = 30.00$ ← Let x represent the number of pairs of socks.

$16.95 - 16.95 + 2.35x = 30.00 - 16.95$ ← Use the subtraction property of equality. Subtract 16.95
$2.35x = 13.05$ from both sides.

$\dfrac{2.35x}{2.35} = \dfrac{13.05}{2.35}$ ← Use the division property of equality. Divide each
     side by 2.35.

$x = 5.55$

You can buy 5 pairs of socks. The solution to the equation is not a whole number, but the answer to the probem must be a whole number to make sense.

Fig. 4.23. Examples of problems that highlight the properties of equality

---

Problem:

A muffin recipe calls for $\dfrac{2}{3}$ cup of flour. You have $5\dfrac{1}{2}$ cups of flour. How many full batches of muffins can you make?

Solution:

$\dfrac{2}{3}x = 5\dfrac{1}{2}$ ←Let x represent the number of batches.

$\dfrac{3}{2} \cdot \dfrac{2}{3}x = \dfrac{3}{2} \cdot \left(5\dfrac{1}{2}\right)$ ← Multiply each side by the multiplicative inverse (reciprocal) of $\dfrac{2}{3}$.

$\dfrac{3}{2} \cdot \dfrac{2}{3}x = \dfrac{3}{2} \cdot \dfrac{11}{2}$

$1x = \dfrac{33}{4}$

$x = 8\dfrac{1}{4}$

You can make $8\dfrac{1}{4}$ batches, or 8 full batches of muffins.

Fig. 4.24. Example of a problem that highlights the multiplicative inverse property

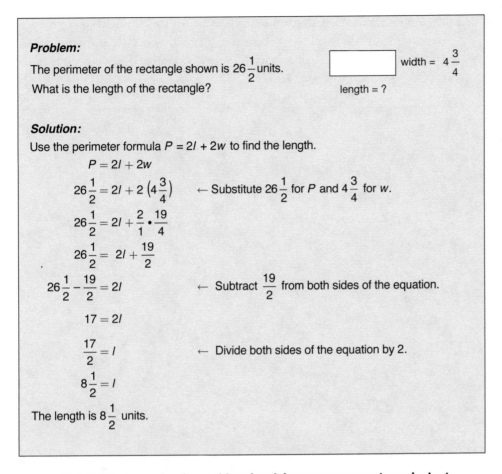

Problem:

The perimeter of the rectangle shown is $26\frac{1}{2}$ units. What is the length of the rectangle?

width = $4\frac{3}{4}$

length = ?

Solution:

Use the perimeter formula $P = 2l + 2w$ to find the length.

$$P = 2l + 2w$$

$$26\frac{1}{2} = 2l + 2\left(4\frac{3}{4}\right) \quad \leftarrow \text{Substitute } 26\frac{1}{2} \text{ for } P \text{ and } 4\frac{3}{4} \text{ for } w.$$

$$26\frac{1}{2} = 2l + \frac{2}{1} \cdot \frac{19}{4}$$

$$26\frac{1}{2} = 2l + \frac{19}{2}$$

$$26\frac{1}{2} - \frac{19}{2} = 2l \quad \leftarrow \text{Subtract } \frac{19}{2} \text{ from both sides of the equation.}$$

$$17 = 2l$$

$$\frac{17}{2} = l \quad \leftarrow \text{Divide both sides of the equation by 2.}$$

$$8\frac{1}{2} = l$$

The length is $8\frac{1}{2}$ units.

Fig. 4.25. Example of a problem involving measurement, equivalent equations, and rational numbers

Strengthening Understanding through Connections

In grade 7 students make connections among their growing understandings of the structure of number and operations, specifically multiplication and division, as they learn how to determine if a counting number greater than 1 is prime or composite. The concepts of prime and composite come into play often as students analyze a rational number as to whether it is in simplest form, determine whether a rational number can be represented by a terminating decimal, and multiply rational numbers by identifying common factors in the numerator and denominator of the product.

Students learn that a *prime number* is a positive integer with exactly two positive integral factors—the number itself and 1. They learn that a positive integer with more than two positive integral factors is *composite*. And, since 1 has only one positive integral factor, it is neither prime nor composite; it is the *multiplicative identity*. Students then connect this understanding of prime numbers to the fundamental theorem of arithmetic, which says that every composite number can be written as a unique product of prime factors, order aside. For example, 12 can be written as 2 × 2 × 3. After students learn how to use exponents, they will write the prime factorization as 2^2 × 3. Students learn that a tree diagram can be a useful tool to organize the prime factors of a number, as shown in figure 4.26.

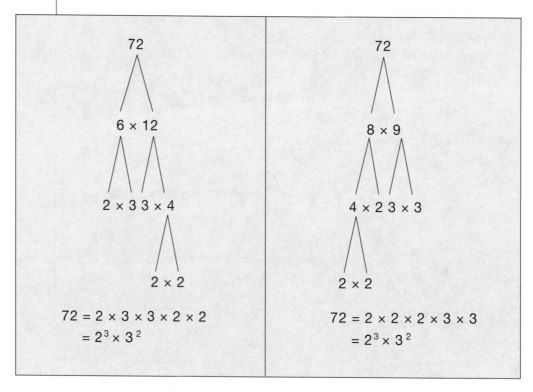

Fig. 4.26. Two factor trees that show the prime factorization of 72

Students can apply their understanding of prime factorization as they work with rational numbers. Specifically, they can use prime factorization to find the least common multiple (LCM) and greatest common factor (GCF) of a set of numbers, as shown in figure 4.27.

Students also connect their work with rational numbers to the application of percentages in making and interpreting histograms and circle graphs. Students learn that a histogram is a graph that uses bars to display data that are organized in intervals. Students can use percents to interpret the data in a histogram, as shown in figure 4.28.

Students also learn how to apply rational numbers as they use percents to make and interpret circle graphs. A circle graph represents each type of data as a sector of a circle. Each sector represents a fraction, or percent, of the data. The sum of the fractions that the sections represent is 1. The sum of the percents that the sections represent is 100 percent. A circle graph is useful to display data as part of a whole. Because percents can be used to display data on a circle graph, students can apply their understanding of percent to make a circle graph. If students are given data, they can determine what percent of the data is represented by each section. Then they can use proportions to find the size of each section so that they can graph the data, as shown in figure 4.29.

Focusing on Understanding the Rational Number System

Least Common Multiple

Use the LCM of 20 and 15 to write $\frac{3}{20}$ and $\frac{5}{12}$ as fractions with common denominators.

1. A common denominator for $\frac{3}{20}$ and $\frac{5}{12}$ is the LCM of 20 and 12.

   To find the LCM of 20 and 12, write the prime factorization of each number:
   $$20 = 2 \times 2 \times 5$$
   $$12 = 2 \times 2 \times 3$$

2. The LCM of 20 and 12 is the least number that can be divided evenly by both 20 and 12, so the LCM must include at least as many of each prime factor as there are in either number. Therefore, the LCM of 20 and 12 needs two factors of 2, one factor of 3, and one factor of 5.
   $$2 \times 2 \times 3 \times 5 = 60$$

3. Use the LCM of 60 as the common denominator, and find the equivalent fractions:
   $$\frac{3}{20} = \frac{3 \times 3}{20 \times 3} = \frac{9}{60} \quad \rightarrow \quad \frac{5}{12} = \frac{5 \times 5}{12 \times 5} = \frac{25}{60}$$

Greatest Common Factor

Use the GCF of 30 and 72 to write $\frac{30}{72}$ in simplest form.

1. A fraction in simplest form has no common factors in the numerator and denominator except 1. To eliminate common factors, we can divide the numerator and denominator by the greatest common factor of 30 and 72. To find the GCF of 30 and 72, write the prime factorization of the numerator and denominator:
   $$30 = 2 \times 3 \times 5$$
   $$72 = 2 \times 2 \times 2 \times 3 \times 3$$

2. The GCF of 30 and 72 is the greatest number that can divide into both 30 and 72 evenly, so the GCF can include only the prime factors that both numbers have in common. Therefore, the GCF of 30 and 72 has one factor of 2 and one factor of 3:
   $$2 \times 3 = 6$$

3. Divide the numerator and denominator by the GCF of 6 to simplify the fraction:
   $$\frac{30}{72} = \frac{30 \div 6}{72 \div 6} = \frac{5}{12}$$

Fig. 4.27. Using prime factorization to find LCM and GCF

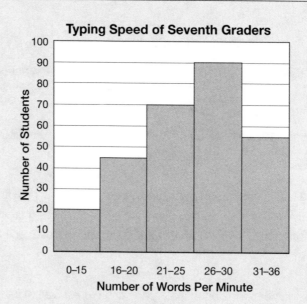

What percent of the seventh graders can type 21 to 25 words per minute?

$$\frac{x}{100} = \frac{70}{280}$$
$$280x = 7000$$
$$x = \frac{7000}{280}$$
$$x = 25$$

So 25 percent of the seventh graders can type 21 to 25 words per minute.

Can more than 50 percent of the seventh graders type more than 25 words per minute? How do you know?

90 + 55 = 145 students can type more than 25 words per minute.

$$\frac{x}{100} = \frac{145}{280}$$
$$280x = 14,500$$
$$x = \frac{14,500}{280}$$
$$x \approx 51.8$$

So about 52 percent of the seventh graders can type more than 25 words per minute, which is greater than 50 percent.

Fig. 4.28. Using percent to interpret histograms

Problem:
The table shows the amount of money Janice's art club spent on different items. Janice makes a circle graph to display the budget. What does her circle graph look like?

Category	Amount Spent ($)
Shirts	112
Pins	84
Trips	56
Supplies	148

Solution:
1. Find what percent of the whole budget that each amount represents.

$112 + 84 + 56 + 148 = 400$; the club spent $400 in all.

Shirts:
$$\frac{112}{400} = \frac{x}{100}$$
$$400x = 11{,}200$$
$$x = \frac{11{,}200}{400}$$
$$x = 28$$

The club spent 28% of the $400 on shirts.

Pins
$$\frac{84}{400} = \frac{x}{100}$$
$$400x = 8400$$
$$x = \frac{8400}{400}$$
$$x = 21$$

The club spent 21% of the $400 on pins.

Trips:
$$\frac{56}{400} = \frac{x}{100}$$
$$400x = 5600$$
$$x = \frac{5600}{400}$$
$$x = 14$$

The club spent 14% of the $400 on trips.

Supplies:
$$\frac{148}{400} = \frac{x}{100}$$
$$400x = 14{,}800$$
$$x = \frac{14{,}800}{400}$$
$$x = 37$$

The club spent 37% of the $400 on supplies.

2. Organize the percents in a table.

Category	Percent of Budget
Shirts	28%
Pins	21%
Trips	14%
Supplies	37%

(Continued on next page)

Fig. 4.29. Using percent to make circle graphs

3. Then find the number of degrees in each sector of the circle. Round the degree measure to the nearest degree if necessary.

Shirts:

$$\frac{28}{100} = \frac{x}{360}$$

$$100x = 10,800$$

$$x \approx 101$$

The "Shirts" sector is about 101°.

Pins:

$$\frac{21}{100} = \frac{x}{360}$$

$$100x = 7650$$

$$x \approx 76$$

The "Pins" sector is about 76°.

Trips:

$$\frac{37}{100} = \frac{x}{360}$$

$$100x = 13,320$$

$$x \approx 133$$

The "Trips" sector is about 50°.

Supplies:

$$\frac{37}{100} = \frac{x}{360}$$

$$100x = 13,320$$

$$x \approx 133$$

The "Supplies" sector is about 133°.

4. Use a protractor to make the circle graph. Label the graph.

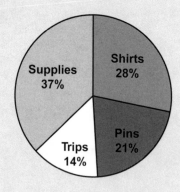

Fig. 4.29. Using percent to make circle graphs—*Continued*

Students can also use percents to interpret circle graphs, as shown in figure 4.30.

Problem:

The circle graph shows the sales at a local toy store for one week. What percent of the sales was sports equipment?

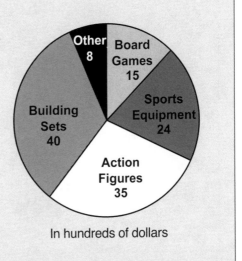

Solution:

Find what percent of 122 is 24.

$$\frac{24}{122} = \frac{p}{100}$$

$$122p = 2400$$

$$p = \frac{2400}{122}$$

$$p \approx 19.7$$

19.7% of the sales was sports equipment.

Fig. 4.30. Using percent to interpret circle graphs

Connections in later grades

In later grades, students will continue working with rational numbers when they use exponents and scientific notation to describe very large and very small numbers. For example, the equation $0.0015 = 1.5 \times 10^{-3}$, showing 0.0015 in scientific notation, contains rational numbers.

Students' knowledge of rational numbers will enable them to understand, by contrast, the concept of irrational numbers. Then, when they use square roots to solve nonlinear equations and to apply the Pythagorean theorem, they will be able to understand that some results are rational and some results are irrational, as illustrated in figure 4.31.

In later grades, students will also develop an understanding of the concept of function and how linear equations can be studied as functions. They will translate among geometric (graphical), numerical (tabular), verbal, and algebraic representations of linear functions in which the algebraic representation involves rational numbers, for example,

$$f(x) = -\frac{2}{3}x - 1.$$

Nonlinear Equations		Pythagorean Therom	
$x^2 = \dfrac{9}{4}$ $x = \sqrt{\dfrac{9}{4}}$ $x = \dfrac{3}{2}$ or $-\dfrac{3}{2}$	$x^2 = 14$ $x = \sqrt{14}$ $x \approx 3.74$ or -3.74	$a^2 + b^2 = c^2$ $3^2 + 5^2 = c^2$ $9 + 25 = c^2$ $34 = c^2$ $\pm\sqrt{34} = c$	$a^2 + b^2 = c^2$ $a^2 + 6^2 = (7.5)^2$ $a^2 + 36 = 56.25$ $a^2 = 20.25$ $a = \sqrt{20.25}$ $a = 4.5$ or -4.5
The solution is rational.	The solution is irrational; its approximate value is 3.74 or −3.74.	The solution is irrational.	The solution is rational.
		Note: Although the solutions to the square roots can be negative or positive, in the instance of the Pythagorean theorem, only positive solutions make sense.	

Fig. 4.31. Examples that illustrate rational and irrational numbers

Students will relate systems of equations that involve rational numbers to pairs of lines that intersect, are parallel, or are the same line in the plane and understand that the solution to a system of two equations in two unknowns is a solution to both equations. They will use rational numbers to analyze and solve problems using linear equations and systems of linear equations. The equations will contain rational x-coefficients and rational y-intercepts, and their solutions will contain rational numbers, as shown in figure 4.32.

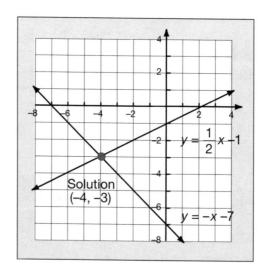

Fig. 4.32. Graph of a system of two linear equations in two unknowns involving rational numbers

Developing Depth of Understanding

What activities can you give students to help them see the need for the set of rational numbers? How can you facilitate students' transition from using positive and negative integers and whole numbers to using the set of rational numbers, including negative fractions and decimals?

References

Donovan, M. Suzanne, and John D. Bransford, eds. *How Students Learn: Mathematics in the Classroom.* Washington, D.C.: National Research Council, 2005.

Fuson, Karen C., and Aki Murata. "Integrating the NRC Principles and the NCTM Process Standards: Cognitively Guided Teaching to Individualize Instruction within Whole-Class Activities and Move All Students within Their Learning Path." *National Council of Supervisors of Mathematics Journal* 10 (Spring 2007): 72–91.

Kilpatrick, Jeremy, Jane Swafford, and Bradford Findell, eds. *Adding It Up: Helping Children Learn Mathematics.* Washington, D.C.: National Research Council, 2001.

Lampert, Magdalene. "Choosing and Using Mathematical Tools in Classroom Discourse." In *Advances in Research on Teaching,* vol. 1, edited by Jere Brophy, pp. 223–64. Greenwich, Conn.: JAI Press, 1989.

Mack, Nancy K. "Learning Fractions with Understanding: Building on Informal Knowledge." *Journal for Research in Mathematics Education* 21 (January 1990): 16–32.

Mirra, Amy. *Focus in Grades 3–5.* Reston, Va.: National Council of Teachers of Mathematics, 2008.

———. *Focus in Grades 6–8.* Reston, Va.: National Council of Teachers of Mathematics, 2009.

National Council of Teachers of Mathematics (NCTM). *Curriculum and Evaluation Standards for School Mathematics.* Reston, Va.: NCTM, 1989.

———. *Principles and Standards for School Mathematics.* Reston, Va.: NCTM, 2000.

———. *Curriculum Focal Points for Prekindergarten through Grade 8 Mathematics: A Quest for Coherence.* Reston, Va.: NCTM, 2006.

———. *Focus in Grade 3.* Reston, Va.: NCTM, 2009a.

———. *Focus in Grade 4.* Reston, Va.: NCTM, 2009b.

———. *Focus in Grade 5.* Reston, Va.: NCTM, 2009c.

———. *Focus in High School Mathematics: Reasoning and Sense Making.* Reston, Va.: NCTM, 2009d.

———. *Focus in Grade 6.* Reston, Va.: NCTM, 2010a.

———. *Focus in Grade 8.* Reston, Va.: NCTM, 2010b.

Rachlin, Sid, Kathleen Cramer, Connie Finseth, Linda Cooper Foreman, Dorothy Geary, Seth Leavitt, and Margaret Schwan Smith. *Navigating through Number and Operations in Grades 6–8.* Reston, Va.: NCTM, 2006.

Webb, David C., Nina Boswinkel, and Truus Dekker. "Beneath the Tip of the Iceberg: Using Representations to Support Student Understanding." *Mathematics Teaching in the Middle School* 14 (September 2008): 110–13.